Y0-BZT-170

GUIDE TO
Freshwater Fishes
of New York

by
Daniel J. Decker
Ronald A. Howard, Jr.
W. Harry Everhart
John W. Kelley

illustrated by
Tom Parker

An extension publication from the Department of Natural Resources, College of Agriculture and Life Sciences at Cornell University

in cooperation with the Bureau of Fisheries, Division of Fish and Wildlife, New York State Department of Environmental Conservation

Illustrations funded by the American Wildlife Research Foundation, Inc.

Contents

Authors

Daniel J. Decker is an associate professor and department chair; **Ronald A. Howard, Jr.** is a former extension associate; and **W. Harry Everhart** and **John W. Kelley** are professors emeriti, Department of Natural Resources, College of Agriculture and Life Sciences at Cornell University, Ithaca, NY 14853.

Acknowledgments

The authors would like to acknowledge the assistance and cooperation of several persons during preparation of this bulletin. Many regional and central office staff in the Division of Fish and Wildlife, New York State Department of Environmental Conservation, provided distribution and life history information on various fishes; the assistance of these biologists was very much appreciated.

We thank Carl Parker, chief of the Bureau of Fisheries, for his review of the manuscript.

Cornell faculty members Drs. Dwight Webster and Edward Brothers provided information on field characters for some of the fishes.

A special thanks is due Dr. Edward C. Raney, professor emeritus for his cooperation in providing distribution information for most of the fish species in the bulletin.

The authors are indebted to the American Wildlife Research Foundation, Inc., for providing a grant to help with the line drawings in the illustrated keys. The illustrations were prepared by Tom Parker.

Michael Duttweiler, assistant program leader, New York Sea Grant Extension Program, made several useful suggestions on the original salmonid key.

Typing was done by Barbara Kirk, Deborah Maskin, Cindy Snyder, Eileen Stanturf, Deborah Walsh, and Charlotte Westbrook.

Preface

"What kind of fish is that?" is a question frequently asked Sea Grant specialists, state fisheries biologists, and extension specialists by amateur naturalists, beginning fishermen, and experienced anglers fishing in unfamiliar waters. The importance of the question to anglers is easily realized after looking through the fishing regulations in the New York State fishing guide. You'd better know what kind of fish you've just caught! Chances are that special regulations exist concerning when and where it can be fished for as well as what size it must be and how many can be kept.

Two problems in fish identification by anglers frequently arise: (1) many anglers refer to fish by common names different from those used in the New York fishing regulations; and (2) some anglers, especially beginners, are not familiar with techniques used to tell fish apart. Misidentifying fish prevents an angler from properly interpreting fishing regulations and may cause unintentional violations of fish and wildlife laws, upsetting the best management efforts.

This guide is designed to help anglers,

naturalists, and others identify fish commonly found in New York State's fresh waters. A series of nontechnical keys has been developed to simplify identification from readily observable external features. Several fine technical keys are available for fish identification, but they require considerable knowledge of fish biology and anatomy (see "References"). Since anglers need to identify their catch quickly, the keys in this guide rely primarily on field marks — differences in colors, patterns, and markings that are visible in fresh fish. Some variation among fish of a species can be expected with field marks, but those used in the keys should permit you to identify most fishes found in the state. Please note that although more than food and sport fish are covered, not every species of fish living in New York is included in the key. Some "family" characteristics are given without detailed descriptions of every species in the family (for example, minnow family). All fish presently regulated in New York are in the key. Common and scientific names used in this guide are in accordance with those currently recommended and used by the American Fisheries Society.

Most fishes present in New York waters can also be found in waters throughout the northeastern United States. This guide will be useful for identifying those fish. However, several species present in other waters do not occur in New York State waters and therefore are not included in this guide.

In addition to the nontechnical keys, brief descriptions of the habitat, food requirements, natural history, and general distribution in New York are given for the fishes.

Before diving headlong into the keys, be sure to read the brief introductory section concerning the parts of a fish. A few terms used in the keys may be unfamiliar and are explained in the introduction.

About Fish

Fish easily outnumber all other vertebrate animals (animals with backbones) combined. About 40,000 different kinds of fish exist in the world today; about 218 species are present in New York's fresh or brackish waters. Fish are cold-blooded, backboned animals adapted for life in water. Their fins are specialized for mobility in water, and their gills enable them to obtain oxygen from water.

Fish are superbly adapted for moving through water, a fact easily confirmed by observing their swimming movements. In general, their streamlined shape may be described as torpedo- or cigarlike. Some fish are very round, like the eels, and some are more flattened from side to side (compressed), like the sunfishes.

Covering the outer surface of fish is a layer of mucus produced by glands in the skin. This mucous layer protects fish from external infection. (Consequently, fishermen should wet their hands before handling a fish they intend to release; handling with dry hands could remove enough of the protective mucous covering to leave fish exposed to fungous and bacterial infections.) Directly beneath the mucus is a thin layer of skin covering the embedded scales.

Scales develop soon after the fish is hatched, and scale growth reflects changes in the growth of a fish. Age of a fish can be determined from the number of year marks on a scale, and periods of good and poor growth can be detected from the spacing of these growth rings. Most of New York's freshwater fish have scales that are either cycloid or ctenoid. Cycloid scales are usually small and embedded deeply in the skin, such as those of trout and salmon. Ctenoid scales have several rows of small spines along their exposed (posterior) edge, making the fish feel rough or spiny when touched. Bass and sunfish are examples of fish with ctenoid scales.

Catfish and sculpin do not have scales.

It is useful to know a few general terms for referring to body characteristics of fish. *Anterior* means toward the front or head end of the body. *Posterior* refers to the rear of the body. *Dorsal* refers to the upper portion of the fish. *Ventral* is the underside or lower part of the body. *Lateral* refers to the sides. *Median* means along the midline of the back and abdomen, the fish being divided into right and left halves.

Figure 1 shows a generalized fish. It does not represent any particular kind of fish, but was created to include most of the types of structures found on the fish you are likely to encounter. These structures are referred to in the key that begins on page 14. Your familiarity with them is important to your ease in using the key.

Fish fins are thin folds of skin supported by rays, spines, or both. Fish are often referred to as being *soft rayed*, like the trout, or *spiny rayed*, like the bass. Rays are finely segmented, often branched, and flexible, while spines are unsegmented, unbranched, and stiff. Because their number is reasonably constant in any one fish species, counting rays and spines is frequently helpful in distinguishing between closely related fishes.

Fins are classified according to their structure and their location on the fish. As shown in figure 1, there are six different kinds of fins. They are divided into two categories, median fins and paired fins. The dorsal, adipose, caudal, and anal fins are median fins. The pectoral and pelvic fins are paired fins. Not all fish species have all of these fins. Although a fish swims primarily by muscular movements of its body, it depends on the caudal fin for lending power to the movements, on the dorsal and anal fins for stabilizing the movements, and on the pectoral and pelvic fins for steering and maneuvering.

The dorsal and adipose fins are located on the dorsal midline of a fish. The dorsal

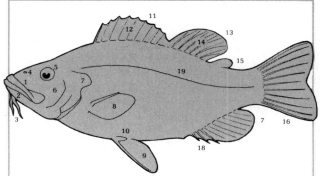

Figure 1. General characters commonly used in identifying fish.

1. Upper jaw (premaxillary and maxillary bones)
2. Lower jaw (mandible)
3. Barbel
4. Nostril
5. Eye
6. Cheek
7. Gill cover
8. Pectoral fin
9. Pelvic fin
10. Pelvic axillary process
11. Spiny dorsal fin
12. Fin spine
13. Soft dorsal fin
14. Fin ray
15. Adipose fin
16. Caudal fin (tail)
17. Anal fin
18. Anal spine
19. Lateral line

fin may be supported by soft rays, stiff spines, or both. The adipose fin is a small, fatty fin located between the dorsal fin and the tail.

The tail is called the caudal fin. It can be heterocercal (sharklike), a portion of the backbone extending slightly into the upper lobe, which projects farther rearward than the lower lobe. Only a few "primitive" fish have this type of tail. It can also be homocercal (symmetrical); most fish have this type of tail. A homocercal tail can be either square, pointed, rounded, slightly forked, or deeply forked. In a homocercal tail the backbone ends at the middle of the base of the fin. (For our purposes in this guide, we will refer to the caudal fin simply as the tail.)

A single anal fin is located on the ventral midline of a fish, between the anus and tail. The anal fin is entirely soft rayed

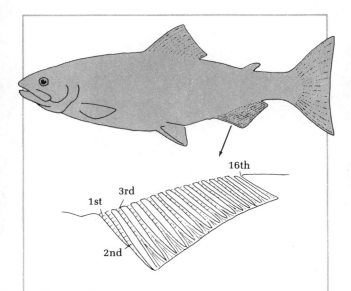

Figure 2. Fin ray counting.

in most fish, but in some species the first two or three rays are spiny. The fins found just behind each gill cover are the pectoral fins. On some fish, these fins have stiff spines. The pair of pelvic fins is located ventrally and varies in position on different fishes from being directly under the pectoral fins to directly in front of the anus. At the anterior base of the pelvic fins may be a small, bony projection called the pelvic axillary process.

The shape of the anal fin and the number of anal fin rays are helpful in identifying several fish. In some cases, comparing the depth of the anal fin to the length of its base helps; in others, counting the number of rays in the anal fin is useful (fig. 2). To count anal fin rays, start with the first short ray nearest the anus; that is ray number one. You will notice that most of the rays fan out at the end. Don't count each little branch of this fan — count only the major portion of the ray near the fin base, as shown in figure 2. The last ray may be very short, only the fanned out end showing. Nevertheless, it should be counted as a ray. The number of anal fin

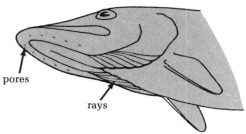

Figure 3. Branchiostegal (sensory) pores, and branchiostegal rays.

rays indicated for fish in the key are those most commonly found in the majority of individuals for a given kind of fish. Occasionally, you will find a fish that has more or less than the number designated.

Gill covers, or opercula, are located on each side of the fish's head. They protect the gills (a fish's respiratory organ) and gill rakers (fingerlike projections on the gill arches). The size, shape, scale pattern, and color of the gill covers vary by species. The gill covers of some species have an opercular lobe, or gill flap, which sticks out on the posterior edge of the gill cover; other fish have a spine on the gill cover. All these variations are aids in fish identification.

The section of the head in front of the gill cover and under the eye is the cheek. The outer circumference of the eye is called the orbit. The nostrils are holes in the snout. On some fish they are partially covered by a fleshy flap called a septum. A fish's upper jaw is composed of two bones called the maxillary and premaxillary. The premaxillary extends from the forward tip of the mouth back to a point where the bone widens; from this point back is the maxillary. The lower jaw is called the mandible.

Some fish have fleshy, whiskerlike projections around their mouths which are called barbels. On the underside of the lower jaw of some fish are holes called branchiostegal pores and ridges called branchiostegal rays (fig. 3). The number of these is an aid to the identification of fish in the pike family.

Fish teeth are varied. Some fish have firm, conical teeth, whereas others lack noticeable teeth or have teeth that are very small and weakly held in place. Some have canine teeth, and others have vomerine teeth. The vomer is a toothed bone located in the roof of some fishes' mouths. The number and placement of these vomerine teeth are useful clues to a fish's identity.

The lateral line on a fish is a visible line of porelike, sensory openings along the side of a fish. The absence or presence and length of the lateral line also are important aids in fish identification.

Fish obtain oxygen from water passing over the gills. Closing the gill covers, opening the mouth, and expanding the cheeks causes water to flow in. Closing the mouth, contracting the cheeks, and opening the gill covers causes water to flow out over the gills. Gills are made up of a fine network of small blood vessels with walls so thin that oxygen can pass from the water into the blood and carbon dioxide can pass from the blood into the water.

Fish reproduction is interesting and of great importance to correct management of the fishery concerned. Although internal fertilization and development are known in fish, New York fish fertilize their eggs externally. Development, therefore, takes place outside the body of the female. In some fish, the males take on spawning coloration near and during spawning time. Approach of spawning season is the signal in most fish for a migration to their spawning area. Distances traveled may be many miles, as with Pacific salmon, or only a few feet, as with lake trout. Certain fish, particularly minnows and suckers, develop hard projections or tubercles on the fins, head, and body during the breeding season. These tubercles are more pronounced on males and are used in grasping the female and in defending the spawning area.

Some fishes build nests. Female trout and salmon have the job of preparing the nest, but neither parent assumes any responsibility once the eggs are fertilized and covered. Males of the sunfish family prepare the nest and remain to guard the eggs and young. Many fish — pike and white bass, for example — prepare no nest but merely broadcast the eggs, which lie on the bottom among the rocks or aquatic plants. Most fish are polygamous, several males fertilizing the eggs of the female or the eggs of several females being fertilized by a single male.

Fish eat almost every conceivable form of food. The mouth and teeth serve as clues to the food habits of fish. The large teeth in the mouth of the northern pike leave no doubt about the carnivorous food habits of this species. Likewise, lack of teeth in the mouth of a gizzard shad indicate that this fish is primarily a plankton feeder. Fish may travel together and feed in schools or may seek their food alone. Some species make characteristic daily migrations, coming into the shallow areas in the evening where they are readily taken by hook and line. Temperature plays an important part in feeding and other activities of fish.

Fish perceive the world around them with the same set of senses we have, but fish are adapted and specialized for life in water. For example, their eyes see short distances only. Fish detect colors much as we do, but their eyes are adapted to see light rays modified when passing from air into water.

To most fish, the sense of smell plays an important role, and the olfactory sense is developed to a much higher degree in fish than in land animals. Fish nostrils lead into sacs containing the olfactory organs, and the nostrils are used only for the sense of smell. Water cannot pass through them to the gills for respiration.

A fish has no visible external ear, nor does it have a middle ear to help transmit sound waves to the inner ear, where the sound waves are actually picked up and transmitted to the brain. Despite the lack of external and middle ears, fish sense vibrations, or sounds, at nearly the same frequencies as we do on land. Sound waves are transmitted much better in water than in air, and a fish's body is only slightly denser than the water around it, so sound waves encounter little interference in passing directly into the inner ear. Some fish, such as minnows, suckers, and catfishes, have an additional hearing apparatus consisting of a series of delicate bones linking the inner ear with the air bladder, the air bladder serving as an amplifier.

The air bladder is an important organ for life in water. Primarily a hydrostatic organ, it helps the fish maintain position in water. In most fish, the air bladder also serves to equalize internal pressure at different depths. The air bladder is used by some fish to produce grunting sounds by vibrating muscle fibers over the surface. Some fish can supplement the respiration of the gills by gulping air from the surface into the air bladder, using it as a lung.

An important sensory organ for life in water is the lateral line, prominent on the side of the fish and radiating out onto the head. Tiny sensory pores of the lateral line detect minute pressure changes and low-intensity vibrations.

Development of the sense of taste in fish is related to the importance of this sense in their daily lives. In catfish, for example, the sense of taste is of major importance. A striking difference between fish and land animals is that taste buds are not restricted to the mouth in fish, but may be found on the barbels, fins, and even on the body surface, as in catfish.

How to Use This Guide

Before attempting to identify a fish, the reader should become acquainted with the material in the preceding section and with figure 1, which represents a generalized fish (no fish has all the characteristics shown) and illustrates the location of the principal characters used throughout the keys.

The identification keys simply represent a series of choices that separate the kinds of fish on the basis of easily recognized characteristics. First, determine the family to which the fish belongs by consulting the key to families on page 14. To use this key, you select from the first pair of statements the description that best fits your fish; then go to the next pair of statements indicated by the reference number after the one you selected. Be sure to consider all the characteristics given in the description, not just one. Repeating the process, you finally isolate the family of the fish you have in hand. Some families of fish found in New York have only a single representative; once the family is determined, the name of the fish will be known. Other families have several representatives, or species, occurring in New York. In this case, after determining the family to which the fish belongs, turn to the page indicated and proceed through the key to the members of that family until you correctly identify the specific kind of fish. After reading these introductory sections, practice using the key on a fish you are familiar with. Practice is good experience and the best way to learn to use the keys.

Key to Fish Families

1

a. A round, suckerlike disc mouth, lined with rows of horny teeth; no jaws; no paired fins; 7 uncovered gill openings (appear as holes on each side of fish)

Round, suckerlike disc mouth of lamprey

Lamprey Family (Petromyzontidae) p. 29

b. Does not have round, suckerlike disc mouth lined with horny teeth; has true jaws; paired pectoral fins present; one gill opening with gill cover on each side of fish

2

2

a. Pelvic fins absent; body long and cylindrical (snakelike)

American Eel (Anguillidae) p. 34

b. Pelvic fins present; body not snakelike

3

3

a. Backbone extends upward into or partially into upper part of tail (heterocercal and modified heterocercal tail)

4

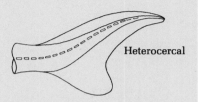

Heterocercal

Modified heterocercal

b. Backbone does not extend into tail (homocercal tail)

6

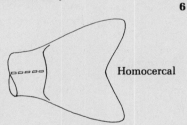

Homocercal

4

a. Tail typical heterocercal; mouth under and behind tip of projecting snout; 4 barbels under snout; no or poorly developed teeth; bony plates on head and body

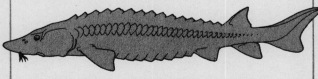

Sturgeon Family (Acipenseridae) p. 30

b. Tail modified heterocercal type; mouth located at tip of snout; no barbels under snout; well-developed teeth present

5

5

a. Jaws very elongated, alligatorlike; body covered with hard, sharp, diamond-shaped scales; dorsal fin short and located posteriorly, near tail; no barbels on snout

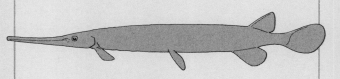

Diamond-shaped
scales of gar

**Gar Family
(Lepisosteidae)** p. 32

b. Jaws not elongated or alligatorlike; body covered with soft scales; dorsal fin very long, extending over most of back and almost to tail; barbels on nostrils; hard, bony plate on throat

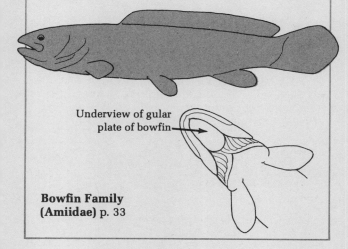

Underview of gular
plate of bowfin

**Bowfin Family
(Amiidae)** p. 33

6

a. Pelvic fins are located relatively far behind the pectorals on the abdomen

7

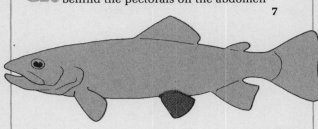

b. Pelvic fins located near the pectorals, either slightly behind, forward or directly under

17

7

a. Adipose fin present

8

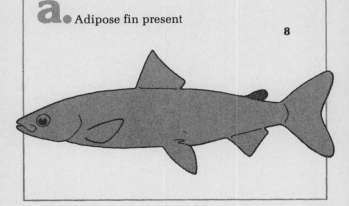

b. Adipose fin absent

12

8

a. Barbels on snout, corner of mouth, and chin; scales absent; single stout spine in dorsal and pectoral fins

Catfish Family (Ictaluridae) p. 99

b. Barbels absent; scales present; pectoral fins without spines

9

9

a. Weak spines on anal and dorsal fin; scales rough; large head

Trout-perch Family (Percopsidae) p. 106

b. Fins without spines; scales smooth

10

10

a. Pelvic axillary process absent

Rainbow Smelt (Osmeridae) p. 57

b. Pelvic axillary process present

11

11

a. Mouth small; upper jaw not extending rearward to below center of eye; teeth on jaws and tongue weak

Whitefish Subfamily (Salmonidae; subfamily Coregoninae) p. 42

b. Mouth large, upper jaw extending back past center of eye or farther; strong conical teeth on jaws and tongue

Salmon and Trout Subfamily (Salmonidae; subfamily Salmoninae) p. 47

12

a. Midline of belly has sawlike keel

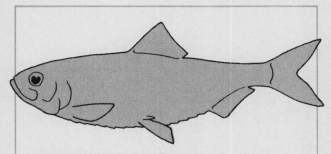

Herring Family (Clupeidae) p. 36

b. Midline of belly without sawlike keel

13

13 _____

a. Head entirely or partially scaled

14

b. Head without scales

16

14 _____

a. Jaws long, extending far forward, snout shaped like a duck's bill; large, sharp teeth; tail forked

Pike Family (Esocidae) p. 60

b. Jaws short; teeth weak; tail rounded

15

15 _____

a. Upper jaw separated from snout by a groove

Groove

**Killifish Family
(Cyprinodontidae) p. 108**

b. Upper jaw not separated from snout by a groove

No groove

Mudminnow Family (Umbridae) p. 59

16

a. Mouth points downward (inferior) and is suckerlike, having thick, fleshy lips; dorsal fin has 10 or more rays; no spines in dorsal or anal fins

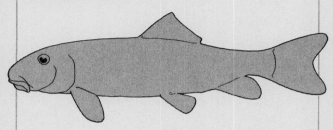

Suckerlike, inferior mouth

Sucker Family (Catostomidae) p. 91

b. Mouth opening toward the front (terminal or subterminal); thin lips; dorsal fin usually with less than 10 rays; if more than 10 rays, spines present in both dorsal and anal fins

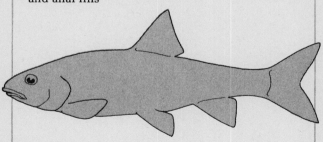

Minnow Family (Cyprinidae) p. 66

17

a. Dorsal fin preceded by isolated dorsal spines

Stickleback Family (Gasterosteidae) p. 108

b. Dorsal fin not preceded by isolated dorsal spines

18

18

a. Body covered with scales

19

b. Body not covered with scales, but may have a patch of small spines or prickles behind pectoral fin; head large; eyes in top of head; pectoral fins large

Sculpin Family (Cottidae) p. 134

19

a. Single barbel on middle of chin; rounded caudal fin; two dorsal fins, the first short and the second long, extending to tail; anal fin nearly as long as second dorsal fin; pelvic fin located in front of pectoral fins

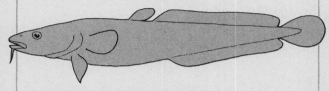

Cod Family (Gadidae) p. 107

b. No barbel on chin

20

20

a. Anal spines 1 or 2

21

b. Anal spines 3 or more, the first of which is short and sometimes difficult to see

22

21

a. Lateral line extends onto the tail; spiny and soft-rayed dorsal fins deeply indented but joined; very blunt, rounded snout; no spine on gill cover

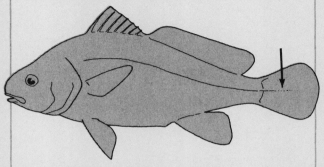

Freshwater Drum (Sciaenidae) p. 133

b. Lateral line does not extend onto the tail; spiny and soft-rayed dorsal fins separate; gill cover usually ends in a spine

Perch Family (Percidae) p. 127

22

a. Well-developed spine on gill covers; spiny and soft-rayed dorsal fins entirely separate or slightly joined at base

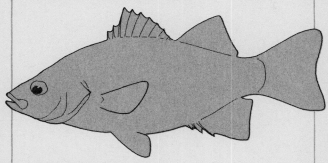

**Temperate Bass Family
(Percichthyidae)** p. 110

b. Gill covers without well-developed spine; spiny and soft-rayed dorsal fins joined (though deeply notched in some species)

Sunfish Family (Centrarchidae) p. 114

Lamprey Family (Petromyzontidae)

Sea Lamprey (Petromyzon marinus)

The sea lamprey is one of the most primitive freshwater fishes existing in New York. This fish, because of its eel-like shape, is sometimes called a lamprey eel, but it is not an eel at all. Lampreys have no jaws, and their skeleton is cartilaginous.

The sea-run form of the lamprey is found regularly and extensively in the Hudson, Delaware, and lower St. Lawrence rivers. It also occurs on the periphery of Long Island. Inland, it is present in Lake Ontario, Lake Champlain, Oneida Lake, Cayuga Lake, and Seneca Lake.

A key characteristic of this fish is its round, suckerlike mouth, lined with concentric rings of teeth. Its tongue also has raspy teeth. These mouth structures are not without purpose, as the adult sea lamprey is a parasitic creature, feeding on the blood and body fluids of other fish. By using its sucker mouth to attach itself to the side of a fish, the lamprey tears away the fish's protective covering (scales and skin). Blood and other body fluids of the host fish are then ingested by the lamprey. A continuous flow of blood is ensured by the secretion of an anticoagulant produced by special glands in the lamprey.

If not landlocked, sea lampreys spend their adult life in the ocean. They return to fresh water to spawn (that is, they are *anadromous*), migrating up streams in May and early June. Males build nests in shallow, swift water by removing cobble and forming a depression on the stream bottom. It is from this characteristic that it gets the scientific name petromyzon, which means "stone sucker." After the female releases her eggs and the male fertilizes them, both adults drift downstream and die.

Several days later, tiny young lampreys called ammocoetes leave the nest and drift downstream to shallow areas that have little current and a mud bottom. There they burrow into the mud. These larvae are nonparasitic and feed on organic material filtered from the water. In 3 to 14+ years, they reach a length of 5 to 7 inches and transform into the adult stage. These new adults move down the streams and out to sea. Upon returning on their spawning run, they will be 2 to 3 feet long.

Sea lampreys are important in New York because of the damage they cause to other desirable fish. Considerable effort has been made to reduce lamprey populations in the larger inland lakes. In these areas, they cause extensive damage to sport fisheries.

Sturgeon Family (Acipenseridae)

Shortnose Sturgeon *(Acipenser brevirostrum)*
Lake Sturgeon *(A. fulvescens)*
Atlantic Sturgeon *(A. oxyrhynchus)*

Sturgeons are primitive fishes with rows of bony, armorlike plates on their sides and a skeleton of cartilage rather than bones. Their tail is heterocercal, the backbone extending into the larger, upper lobe of the tail. This structure is similar to the tail of the shark and some other primitive fishes. Four barbels hang under the sturgeon's long, flattened snout in front of the mouth. Sturgeon are bottom feeders, their sensory barbels being used to detect food and their protruded, tubelike mouth, to suck in bottom-dwelling plants and animals uncovered as they move along the mud.

Sturgeon flesh is of good quality, and the roe (eggs) of Atlantic sturgeon is the well-known delicacy caviar. Sturgeon are no longer important commercially, however, because of their scarcity. They are not usually sought by sport fishermen.

Three members of the sturgeon family inhabit New York waters: shortnose sturgeon (*Acipenser brevirostrum*), lake sturgeon (*A. fulvescens*), and Atlantic sturgeon (*A. oxyrhynchus*). The Atlantic sturgeon is anadromous, ascending large rivers and estuaries to spawn. New York's Atlantic sturgeon population is restricted primarily to the Hudson River. Spawning takes place in the spring at the edge of the saltwater front that moves steadily upstream as runoff decreases. The upper end of the spawning area is near Hyde Park.

Atlantic sturgeon males mature at a length of 4 feet and 12 years old; females, at 6 feet and 18 years old. Females may release as many as 2 million eggs during spawning over a rubble bottom in running water more than 10 feet deep. Spawning runs begin in the spring, but actual spawning may not occur until July. No nest is built, but the adhesive eggs stick to rocks or logs on the bottom. No parental care is given the eggs or young. The young sturgeon hatch a few days after spawning. They may spend up to 4 years in fresh water before moving out to sea.

Recent studies indicate that a population of approximately 150,000 juvenile Atlantic sturgeon may reside in the Hudson River at any one time. This species is not currently fished very heavily; in the past it was harvested in large numbers and often called "Albany beef".

Atlantic sturgeon can reach lengths in excess of 10 feet and weigh several hundred pounds.

Shortnose sturgeon also inhabit the Hudson River. This species spawns in the spring in the upper reaches of the estuary, probably upstream of New Baltimore. Recent studies indicate that a population of approximately 5,000 shortnose sturgeon inhabits the Hudson River. This sturgeon, because of its relatively small population, is listed as an endangered species in both federal and state protective legislation and may not be harvested.

Shortnose sturgeon average 2 feet long and weigh about 3 pounds. Individuals larger than 3 feet and heavier than 10 pounds are uncommon.

The lake sturgeon spawns from early May to late June, but enters spawning streams as soon as the ice is gone. They spawn in swift water, rapids, or the bases of small falls in water 2–15 feet deep. Where suitable spawning streams are unavailable, lake sturgeon may spawn in wave action over ledges or around rocky islands. During spawning, sturgeon lay in groups of two or three — that is, one or two males per female. No nest is built, but the sticky eggs adhere to stones and vegetation. Lake sturgeon do not reach the same size as Atlantic sturgeon, but nevertheless are usually 3–5 feet long and weigh 10–80 pounds. Lake sturgeon may not be harvested because their numbers have dwindled alarmingly — even in the St. Lawrence River where the largest population exists.

Gar Family (Lepisosteidae)

Longnose Gar *(Lepisosteus osseus)*
Spotted Gar *(L. oculatus)*

Gar, like the sea lamprey and sturgeon, are also remnants from primitive times. Their skeletons are part cartilage and part bone. They have long jaws, the snout extending far forward resembling a beak. Both upper and lower jaws are lined with strong, sharp teeth. Their body shape is long and more or less cylindrical. Gars have modified heterocercal tails and hard, diamond-shaped ganoid scales.

The longnose gar is widely distributed in New York. It occurs in Lake George, Lake Champlain, and the St. Lawrence River system. It can be found in Lake Ontario and near the mouths of the larger tributaries; it is present in Cayuga Lake and its northern outlet. In western New York, it is known from the Niagara River, Lake Erie, and Chautauqua Lake. The spotted gar may be found in Lake Erie.

Spotted gar average about 2 feet long and have large dark spots on the dorsal, anal, and caudal fins, the top of the head, and both jaws. The longnose gar averages 3–4 feet long; its head and jaws lack spots.

Gar inhabit warm water, frequenting shallow, weedy areas where they feed on all types of live and dead fish. They spawn in the spring by broadcasting their adhesive eggs in shallow water where the eggs attach to vegetation. No parental care is given the eggs or young.

In addition to gill breathing, gars have a unique air bladder that permits them to obtain oxygen from the air. This air-breathing ability enables gar to survive in polluted waters where other fish species cannot live.

Gar are seldom caught by fishermen and are generally considered a nuisance. Their scales have sharp edges, so they should be handled with gloves. Gar eggs (roe) are extremely toxic, but their rather dry flesh is edible. They are very difficult to prepare and are seldom eaten.

Bowfin Family (Amiidae)

Bowfin *(Amia calva)*

Bowfin are the lone survivors of an earlier primitive family of fish known mostly through fossils. They have retained much cartilage in the skeletal system and have bony plates covering the semicartilaginous skull. A distinctive bony gular plate is located on the under-surface of the throat between the lower jaws. The bowfin's olive-colored body is stout and slightly elongated. A very long dorsal fin helps in identification. Male bowfins have a black spot encircled with a yellow ring at the upper base of the tail; the female has a spot without a circle. In addition to gills, these fish have a modified air bladder, like the gar, that enables them to use surface air and to live in polluted or stagnant water unsuitable for most fish.

The distribution of the bowfin in New York is similar to that of the longnose gar. It occurs in northeastern New York, in Lake George, Lake Champlain, and the St. Lawrence River system (where it is relatively common). It is also found along the shores of Lakes Ontario and Erie. In central New York, it is known from Cayuga Lake, Oneida Lake, and from intermediate waters.

Bowfins are spring spawners. The male constructs a bowl-shaped nest in shallow water and guards the eggs and fry for several weeks. Adult bowfins usually reach a length of about 2 feet and weigh 2–5 pounds, although they may occasionally reach weights of up to 12 pounds.

Bowfins feed on all sorts of aquatic animals — crustaceans, adult insects and larvae, and small fish. Generally, they are a scarce fish of no commercial value. They are dogged fighters when caught on sporting tackle, but their flesh is generally considered poor eating.

Freshwater Eel Family (Anguillidae)

American Eel (Anguilla rostrata)

The American eel is the only freshwater eel in the United States. It is unlike any other fish found in New York, although its body shape and movements are snakelike and similar to the lamprey. Eels differ from lampreys by having pectoral fins, gill covers, and true jaws rather than the lamprey's round, sucker-type mouth. Eels often reach lengths of over 2 feet.

The American eel is abundant in the Hudson and Delaware drainage systems. It is abundant and occurs widely in Long Island waters. This fish has also been found in the Susquehanna River, Finger Lakes, Lake Ontario, St. Lawrence River, and the mouth of the Niagara River.

American eels are unique among freshwater fishes in that they migrate in the fall from fresh water to salt water to spawn (that is, they are *catadromous*). It is believed that adults migrate to the deep Atlantic near Bermuda to spawn and die after spawning. Females have been reported to contain as many as 10 million eggs. Larval eels migrate to the mouths of rivers where they transform into small eels (elvers) 4–6 inches long. It is believed that males remain there and do not get as large as females. In the spring, females move up the streams, usually at night, and make their way into the headwaters where they grow to sexual maturity in 5 to 7 years.

Eels feed on a large variety of both dead and live animal tissue and possibly some plant material. They are most active at night. Eels are readily caught by fishermen and are considered a delicacy by some. A commercial eel fishery exists on the Delaware River and in Lake Ontario. The Hudson River commercial fishery has been temporarily closed because of PCB contamination.

Herring Family (Clupeidae)

1

a. Last ray of dorsal fin greatly elongated and threadlike

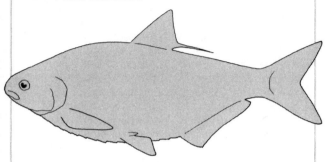

Gizzard Shad *(Dorosoma cepedianum)* p. 40

b. Last ray of dorsal fin not elongated

2

2

a. Silvery patch on cheek deeper than long; mouth extends back to or beyond rear edge of the eye; lower jaw fits into notch of upper jaw when closed; usually 4–6 black spots in horizontal row behind gill cover

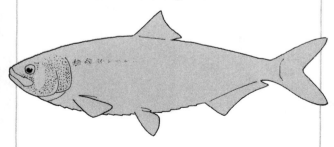

American Shad *(Alosa sapidissima)* p. 39

b. Silvery patch on cheek longer than deep; mouth extends back to only about midpoint of the eye; lower jaw projects forward beyond upper jaw when closed; usually only one black spot near upper rear edge of gill cover

3

3

a. Diameter of eye is greater than distance from front of eye to tip of snout; back distinctly grey green; lining of belly cavity light

Alewife *(Alosa pseudoharengus)* p. 38

b. Diameter of eye is only about as great as distance from front of eye to tip of snout; back distinctly blue green; lining of belly cavity dark

Blueback Herring *(Alosa aestivalis)* p. 38

Herring Family (Clupeidae)

Blueback Herring *(Alosa aestivalis)*

The blueback herring and alewife are of similar shape and general appearance, and distinguishing between them is difficult. Bluebacks tend to have a smaller eye than alewives, with the eye diameter usually smaller than the snout length. As their name implies, these fish often have dark blue backs.

The blueback herring is a common fish on Long Island and in the Hudson and lower Mohawk rivers.

An anadromous fish, the blueback herring spends the greater part of its life in salt water and returns to fresh water to spawn. It usually spawns later in the spring than the alewife, when water temperatures are a bit warmer. During spawning, many eggs are deposited over the stream bottom where they stick to gravel, stones, logs, or other objects. A few surviving, spent fish move back to the sea after spawning. Young fish usually move to sea when about 1 month old and 1½ to 2 inches long.

Bluebacks feed on plankton, various small floating animals, small fish fry, and fish eggs.

Alewife *(Alosa pseudoharengus)*

The alewife is a small herring having a greenish to bluish back and silvery sides with faint dark stripes. It has a small patch of teeth on its tongue.

The sea-run form is common on Long Island and in the Hudson and lower Mohawk rivers. It is also reported from the St. Lawrence River. The landlocked form is common in Lake Ontario, Lake Erie, Finger Lakes area, Oneida Lake, Oswego River system, and Ballston and Round lakes.

Recently it has been introduced in various reservoirs in the upper Delaware drainage system (Pepacton and Cannonsville).

Sea-run alewives move up freshwater streams from the sea to spawn during the period from late April to early June. Spawning takes place in lakes and sluggish stretches of rivers above tidal influence. Landlocked alewives move from deep water to shallow beaches in lakes or move up streams to ponds to spawn in spring.

Females usually move to the spawning areas just before the males. Spawning takes place at night in groups of two or three over a sandy or gravelly bottom. Freshwater females deposit 10,000–12,000 eggs, whereas their sea-run counterparts produce 60,000–100,000 eggs. Eggs are broadcast randomly, are demersal (that is, they sink), and are not particularly adhesive. Adults leave the spawning area after spawning; no care is given eggs or young by the adult fish. In less than a week, the young alewives hatch to begin feeding on minute, free-floating plants and animals. By fall, the young alewives make their way back to the sea or, in the case of landlocked populations, to the deep waters of lakes. Landlocked alewives reach an average length of about 6 inches when adults.

In New York the freshwater alewife (sometimes called sawbelly) is an important forage fish (food) for popular game fish. They have been stocked in some waters specifically to provide food for trout and salmon. Because of their small size, freshwater alewives are not a sport fish; rather, they help to maintain sport fisheries in many inland waters.

American Shad *(Alosa sapidissima)*

Like all members of the herring family, shad have a sawlike keel along the midline of the belly. They are generally silver in color with several (four or five) dark "shoulder spots" along their backs. They have deeply forked tails and long anal fins. Their weight runs between 1½ and 8 pounds.

The American shad is an anadromous fish (lives in salt water, returns to fresh water to spawn). During its spawning runs, it is common in the lower Hudson as far north as Albany and is abundant in the Delaware drainage. This fish is common around and in some tributaries on Long Island.

Shad begin their spawning run in the spring when stream temperatures reach 50–55° F. Males arrive on the spawning grounds ahead of the females, and spawning commences when water temperatures reach 65°F. During spawning, females are accompanied by several males, swimming close to the surface. Spawning takes place in the evening. From about 50,000 to 500,000 eggs are released by the females in open water. The eggs are only slightly heavier than the water and are nonadhesive. They are carried by the water until they eventually settle to the stream bottom. Most shad die after spawning, but some have been known to spawn as many as five times.

Shad eat a variety of plant and animal matter. Shad spawning runs provide a popular sport fishery. Their eggs (roe) are considered a delicacy and their white, flaky flesh is enjoyed by many. There is a commercial fishery for shad on the Hudson River.

Gizzard Shad *(Dorosoma cepedianum)*

Gizzard shad differ from other members of the herring family because the last ray of their dorsal fin is very elongated and threadlike. This deep-bodied fish is generally silver, its upper sides and back being bluish and lower sides, brassy.

Young gizzard shad have a large, dark shoulder spot, but this may be absent on adults.

This fish does not migrate like American shad. It occurs along the shores of Lakes Erie and Ontario, and in Oneida and Cayuga lakes. It has not been reported east of Oneida Lake or on Long Island.

Gizzard shad spawn in early summer, apparently in shallow areas (2–4 feet deep) over sandy, gravelly, or rocky bottoms in lakes and streams. The sticky eggs immediately sink to the bottom, or in streams, move with the current until coming in contact with an object, to which they readily adhere. Females may produce several hundred thousand eggs, which hatch within a week after spawning. The young reach a length of 4–5 inches by autumn. Adults may grow to about 18 inches and 3 pounds, but seldom exceed 12 inches. Generally regarded as a nuisance species, it is seldom sought or eaten by fishermen.

Salmon Family (Salmonidae)
Whitefish Subfamily (Coregoninae)

1

a. Mouth overhung by snout

2

b. Mouth not overhung by snout (mouth terminal)

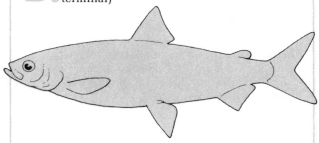

Cisco or Lake Herring *(Coregonus artedii)* p. 43

2

a. Two flaps of skin between the nostrils; weak teeth on jaws; body deeper than it is thick (compressed)

Two flaps between nostrils

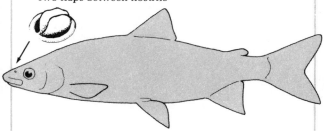

Lake Whitefish *(Coregonus clupeaformis)* p. 44

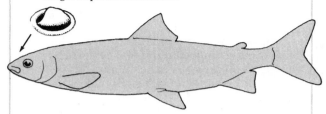

b. Single flap of skin between nostrils; no teeth on jaws; body round in cross-section

Single flap between nostrils

Round Whitefish *(Coregonus cylindraceum)* p. 45

Whitefish Subfamily (Coregoninae)

Whitefishes technically are members of the salmon family, although their small mouth and weak teeth separate them from the salmon and trout. In some areas they are highly regarded as game fish. They are important in many waters as food for various other game fish, and lake whitefish are valuable commercial fish.

Cisco or Lake Herring *(Coregonus artedii)*

Cisco are coldwater fish having dark blue to pale olive backs and silvery sides. All their fins are basically clear, although the anal and pelvic fins are milky on adults. This fish has a protruding lower jaw, forked tail, and an adipose fin. Although size varies greatly, cisco are usually 10–14 inches long and weigh ½–1 pound.

Cisco are widely distributed in lakes across New York. It is present in Lakes Erie and Ontario, tributaries of the St. Lawrence River, Otsego Lake, and in various lakes in the Adirondacks including Lake Champlain. It is also present in the Finger Lakes area and Oneida Lake and has been introduced in other places in recent years (for example, Schoharie Reservoir).

Spawning occurs in late fall, when large spawning groups congregate. Males move to spawning areas before females. In inland lakes, spawning usually takes place in shallow water (3–10 feet deep) over almost any type of bottom, but often over gravel or stony substrate. In large lakes, spawning may occur in shallow water or in deep water. About 20,000–29,000 eggs are deposited on the lake bottom by each female; no parental care is given eggs or young, which hatch early the following spring.

Cisco are a schooling fish, usually frequenting deep water. They move to shallower water in fall as upper waters cool. They are primarily plankton feeders, though insects and small minnows are eaten on occasion. Cisco are an important food for larger game fish.

The flesh of these fish is palatable. It is caught commercially and sought by sport fishermen in the fall using flies and small minnows. It is also caught through the ice on jigs.

Lake Whitefish (Coregonus clupeaformis)

Lake whitefish are generally white with a light olive green shading along the back, which has a slight arch in front. Their fins are white, but the tail has a dark edge. The tail is deeply forked, and an adipose fin is present. The average length for these fish is 18 inches and weight is about 2–4 pounds.

The lake whitefish occurs in Lakes Erie and Ontario, tributaries of the St. Lawrence River, Otsego Lake, and some of the Finger Lakes. It is spotty but widespread in the Adirondacks, including Lake George and Lake Champlain. It has been introduced in lakes elsewhere, but its present distribution in these lakes is questionable.

As its name implies and its distribution illustrates, this fish inhabits large, deep lakes, often the same water areas as lake trout. They spawn in late fall, migrating to shoal areas in lakes or moving up tributary streams. Nests are not built, but several thousand eggs are randomly deposited over the bottom. Parental care is not given to eggs or young. Eggs remain on the spawning ground until they hatch the following spring. Young lake whitefish generally move from the shallow, inshore areas to deeper water by early summer.

Lake whitefish feed primarily on small crustaceans and insects; they sometimes eat small fish.

Lake whitefish are delicious, important commercially in the Great Lakes, and sought by sport fishermen, especially during fall and winter. Besides having palatable flesh, the liver and eggs (sometimes sold as caviar) are also fine eating.

Round Whitefish *(Coregonus cylindraceum)*

The round whitefish has slightly more color than other whitefishes. The back is almost bronze, with silvery sides and white underside. The scales have dark borders. Pectoral fins are amber; pelvic and anal fins also have a slight amber tint. The adipose fin is usually brown spotted. This fish has a small head and is almost round in cross-section. It is slender and elongate, usually about 8–12 inches, weighing about ½ pound or less; specimens of over 20 inches and several pounds have been reported.

In New York, round whitefish are uncommon and sparse, distributed in Lake

Champlain and other Adirondack lakes where they are often referred to as frostfish.

Like other whitefish, round whitefish spawn in the fall. They spawn in gravelly shallows of lakes, at tributary mouths, or occasionally in tributary streams. These fish spawn in pairs, rather than in large spawning schools like the cisco. Females release from about 2,000 to 12,000 eggs, which are abandoned after spawning. Young hatch early in the spring.

The round whitefish frequents water less than 120–150 feet deep. This bottom feeder eats a wide selection of insect larvae, small mollusks, and crustaceans, as well as fish eggs. Their eggs, in turn, are eaten by other bottom feeders (bullheads, white suckers), and the fish themselves are eaten by lake trout. It is of no commercial importance and not often caught by sport fishermen, although it is highly regarded as a food fish by many who have eaten it.

Salmon and Trout Subfamily (Salmoninae)

1 _____

a. Anal fin longer than deep, with 13 or more rays; when anal fin depressed, as indicated by the arrow, the tip of the longest ray does not extend back beyond the base of the fin; one of the 3 Pacific salmon found in New York

2

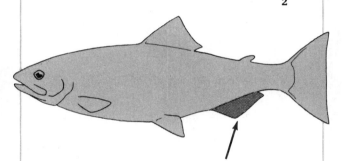

b. Anal fin shorter than deep, with 12 or fewer rays; when anal fin depressed, as indicated by the arrow, the top of the longest ray extends back beyond the base of the fin; either an Atlantic salmon or a trout

4

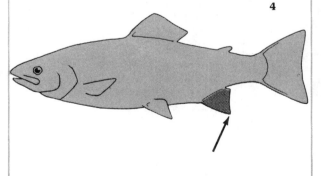

2

a. No black spots, except a few fine black specks on back, usually none on tail, except in spawning adults; interior of mouth light; color generally bluish above lateral line and silvery below it (body bright red or purple and head green in fall spawning condition)

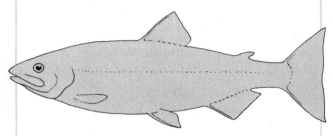

Kokanee Salmon *(Oncorhynchus nerka)* p. 53

b. Black spots on back and tail fin; interior of mouth black

3

3

a. Flesh at base of teeth white; no spots on dorsal fin and lower lobe of tail fin; anal fin rays 13–15; first rays of anal fin reach more than 2/3 of the way to end of fin base when depressed

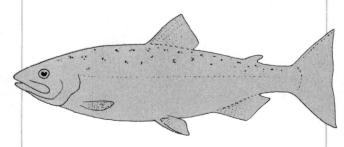

Coho Salmon *(Oncorhynchus kisutch)* p. 53

b. Flesh at base of teeth dark; back, dorsal fin, and both lobes of tail fin covered with many spots; anal fin rays 15–17; first rays of anal fin reach less than 2/3 of the way to end of fin base when depressed

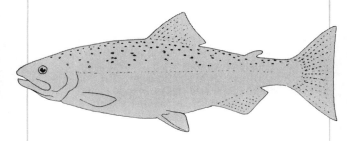

Chinook Salmon *(Oncorhynchus tschawytscha)* p. 53

4

a. Body with black or red spots on light background

5

b. Body with light spots on dark background, no black spots

7

5

a. Tail fin distinctly forked, without black spots (diffuse spots on dorsal lobe of some spawning adults); x- or xx-shaped spots on upper half of sides

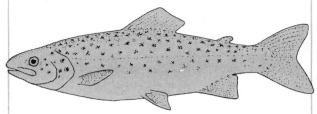

Landlocked Salmon *(Salmo salar)* p. 55

b. Tail fin not distinctly forked; spots usually roundish

6

6

a. Tail fin without black spots or with only a few diffuse ones restricted to upper portion; adipose may be margined with red or orange; both black and red or orange spots present, some black spots may be x shaped; general color brownish yellow, lake-run fish sometimes silvery with only dark spots

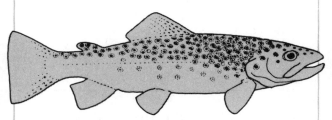

Brown Trout *(Salmo trutta)* p. 55

b. Tail fin heavily spotted; adipose fin not margined with red or orange, but with black spots; no red or orange spots; side spotted and may be marked longitudinally with a faint pink to brilliant red streak; general color often silver in lakes

Rainbow Trout *(Salmo gairdneri)* p. 54

7

a. Pink or reddish spots surrounded by light blue halos; dark "worm track" markings on back; tail fin only slightly forked in smaller fish or squared in larger fish; leading edge of pectoral, pelvic, and anal fins distinctly white

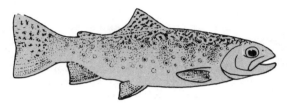

Brook Trout *(Salvelinus fontinalis)* p. 56

b. Body covered with light-colored spots over a darker background, but no pink or red spots; tail fin deeply forked

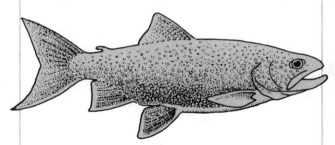

Lake Trout *(Salvelinus namaycush)* p. 56

(Note: Splake are a brook trout × lake trout cross. These hybrids may display intermediate characters and color patterns between the lake trout or brook trout parents. They may have pale pink spots, but never red spots. Tail forked more than brook trout, but not as deeply forked as lake trout.)

Salmon and Trout Subfamily (Salmoninae)

Each kind of salmon and trout (salmonid) in New York is currently managed with specific regulations on size, creel limits, and seasons. Management policies require anglers to identify their catch correctly to apply the proper regulations. Two problems in correct identification frequently arise: (1) many anglers and naturalists use common names for salmonids that differ from those used in fishing regulations; and (2) some anglers, especially beginners, are not familiar with techniques used to differentiate among these sport fishes. Misidentification of fish prevents proper interpretation of fishing regulations and may cause unintentional violations of fish and wildlife laws, upsetting the best management efforts.

Salmonids have fins with soft rays, except the adipose fin — a small, fatty fin located between the dorsal and tail fins — which has no rays. Fins of salmonids lack the stiff spines found on fins of some other fishes, such as sunfish and yellow perch. The dorsal fin is located about midway on the back. The tail varies from being deeply forked on some fish to nearly squared on others.

In summary, salmon and trout are smooth-scaled fish that have: (1) an adipose fin; (2) a large mouth with the jaw extending back beyond the eye; and (3) soft-rayed fins.

Pacific Salmon (*Oncorhynchus* spp.)

Three species of Pacific salmon, kokanee (sockeye), coho (silver), and chinook (king), have been introduced into New York's waters. These fish spend most of their lives in large bodies of water, but run up tributary streams to spawn. Their digestive system degenerates during the spawning run and they die soon after spawning.

Coho Salmon *(Oncorhynchus kisutch)*

The coho salmon is sometimes called a silver salmon because of its silver color. These fish live in the Great Lakes and its tributaries. In the lakes, they feed heavily on alewives (sawbellies). Fall spawning runs bring coho up tributary streams in good numbers where they are available for sport fishing. They also appear in spring in shore catches. These mature fish are usually 3 years old and average 28 inches long and 10 pounds. A few cohos near the 20-pound mark have been caught.

Kokanee Salmon *(Oncorhynchus nerka)*

The kokanee, a landlocked form of the sockeye salmon, is restricted to only a few waters in New York. Kokanee have silvery sides and bellies, except during spawning season when the sides become brick red and the heads are distinctly greenish.

The kokanee does not get nearly as large as its sea-dwelling counterpart, the sockeye. The average size of a kokanee may be only 10–12 inches at sexual maturity, about 4 years old. This size varies from one lake to another, apparently governed by the abundance of food. Kokanee feed almost exclusively on tiny, free-floating plants and animals (plankton).

Chinook Salmon *(Oncorhynchus tschawytscha)*

In New York, chinook salmon, also known as king salmon, are present in Lake Erie and Lake Ontario and run up the tributaries during fall spawning migrations. These fish are taken offshore by trolling and sometimes appear in spring inshore catches. Chinooks usually mature at 3 years of age. They are larger than their cousin the coho — about 34 inches long and 18 pounds. Occasionally, chinook in excess of 40 pounds are caught.

Rainbow Trout *(Salmo gairdneri)*

The rainbow trout's native range was the mountain networks of western North America from the Aleutian Islands to northern Mexico. They were first introduced in New York in the 1880s. These fish have since been stocked in many waters throughout the state.

Rainbow trout may closely resemble coho and chinook salmon when found in large bodies of water. Here, the magnificent color found in other rainbows may be only faintly visible. From this overall silver, the rainbow's color varies. Some have a dark back, a silvery belly, and a brilliant red streak running along the lateral line from below the eye to the tail (the characteristic for which it was named). Rainbows have black spots on their head, gill covers, back, and sides (above and below lateral line), and on the dorsal, adipose, and tail fins.

There are both sea-run and landlocked populations of rainbow trout. The sea-run populations, called steelheads, are most common in the Pacific Northwest. In New York, adult rainbows living in lakes and reservoirs are often called steelheads because of their springtime spawning runs up tributaries (which are similar to the runs made by steelheads) and because of their steel gray, silvery appearance. The spawning behavior of the rainbow and the Atlantic salmon are similar, except that the rainbow spawns in the spring. Young usually remain in their nursery stream for 2 years (and up to 5 years); then they move down into the lake to mature. Rainbows first spawn in about their fourth year. They may spawn several times during their lives. Young trout feed on insects and crustaceans. Larger rainbows feed on fish.

Landlocked Salmon *(Salmo salar)*

Landlocked salmon are Atlantic salmon that spend their entire lives in fresh water. The landlocked salmon generally is found in large, cold, oxygen-rich lakes, which in New York include Lake George, Lake Champlain, Cayuga Lake, and a few other large waters. They are present in some tributaries used as nursery streams. Unlike the Pacific salmon *(Oncorhynchus* spp.), Atlantic and landlocked salmon do not die immediately after spawning, and some survive to spawn again. This fish spawns in inlet or outlet streams in autumn. Nests (redds) are constructed in riffle areas by the female. Young landlocked salmon usually stay in the nursery streams for 1 to 2 years before migrating into the lake. While in the stream, young salmon (parr) feed on insect larvae and other small aquatic creatures. Older salmon living in the lake feed on smelt, alewives, minnows, and other small fish.

Brown Trout *(Salmo trutta)*

The brown trout, a native of Europe, has been distributed throughout the U. S. In New York, the brown trout is found in a wide variety of waters, from brooks and rivers to large lakes and reservoirs.

Browns spawn in the fall. They build nests (redds) on gravelly stream bottoms. Lake-dwelling brown trout spawn in tributary streams. After the eggs are fertilized, the female covers them with fine gravel. The young hatch the following spring.

Brown trout feed on the larval and adult forms of aquatic and terrestrial insects. Other creatures, such as frogs, crustaceans, and fish, are also consumed. Stream-dwelling browns actively feed at night, especially during the summer.

Brook Trout *(Salvelinus fontinalis)*

In New York, brook trout can be found in the cold, clear headwaters of most streams. Cold Adirondack lakes and ponds usually have resident brook trout populations. Some of the largest fish of this species in New York are taken from these waters.

The natural habitat for brook trout can be both stream or lake, but like other salmonids, they thrive in water with low temperatures and high oxygen content. A few coastal populations of brook trout inhabit salt water. These are called salters in New England or sea trout in the Maritimes. Brook trout in the Great Lakes are often called coasters. Brook trout populations are usually comprised of predominately small fish (less than 12 inches). A short life (5 years about maximum), a cold lake or stream environment, and fishing pressure combine to limit size.

Brook trout mature at about 2 years of age and spawn in the fall. Lake-dwelling fish may spawn in streams or along the shoreline of lakes if spring seepage occurs. Occasionally, the lake outlet will be used for spawning. Nests are constructed by the female on gravelly bottoms of streams or lakes.

Young trout feed primarily on insect larvae. Older fish eat an assortment of insects, worms, crustaceans, and small fish.

Lake Trout *(Salvelinus namaycush)*

Lake trout are found in more than 80 New York lakes. They occur in the Finger Lakes, Lake Erie, Lake Ontario, Lake Champlain, Lake George, and many other lakes in the Adirondacks. They have been introduced elsewhere. Lake trout inhabit deep, cold lakes, especially those with boulder-strewn or gravel bottoms. In the far north, where water temperatures remain relatively low, "lakers" sometimes move into rivers connected to lakes to feed. In New York these fish can be found in shallow water near shore only during colder periods of the year. At other times, they are restricted to the depths.

Lake trout spawn in the fall. Areas of a lake with a coarse gravel or boulder bottom are chosen as spawning sites. Males usually enter the spawning area first. Unlike other trout or salmon, no nest is built; the bottom is swept clean by the movements of the fish. After a few days the female enters the area, and several males may spawn in groups with one or more females. No apparent changes in physical appearance occur in lake trout during the spawning season.

The young lake trout eat insects and crustaceans. Larger individuals feed heavily on fish.

Splake (*Salvelinus fontinalis* × *Salvelinus namaycush*)

The splake is a hybrid brook (speckled) trout × lake trout cross. Unlike many hybrids, splake are fertile and able to produce viable young. These fish exhibit a great deal of variation in color and markings. They lack the red spotting of brook trout but have the yellow body spotting of lake trout. Their tails often are slightly forked. The body shape of splake is intermediate between that of brook and lake trout, usually being stockier than lake trout, but not as stocky as brook trout. Splake reach sexual maturity sooner than lake trout and grow larger than brook trout.

Smelt Family (Osmeridae)

Rainbow Smelt (*Osmerus mordax*)

Only one member of the smelt family — the rainbow smelt — is present in New York. This is a small, slender, elongate fish averaging 6–8 inches long. This silvery fish has a complete lateral line, relatively large scales, a large mouth, a forked tail, and an adipose fin.

Sea-dwelling populations of this fish are anadromous, running up freshwater streams to spawn. Freshwater or landlocked smelts are most important in New York. They are found in Lake Erie, the Niagara River, Lake Ontario, the Finger Lakes, and scattered lakes in the Adirondacks. They also are present in Lake George and Lake Champlain. They are fairly common in the Hudson, particularly in the area midway between Manhattan and Albany.

Smelt spawn in spring, when large numbers run up tributary streams. Although spawning usually occurs in streams, in some situations smelt may spawn offshore on gravel shoals. Spawning primarily takes place at night, with two or more males accompanying one female in riffle areas of the stream or along the lake shore. The female releases her 10,000 or more adhesive eggs, which stick to the bottom gravel. During spawning season male smelt have many rough-feeling breeding tubercles on the body which easily distinguish them from the females.

Smelt are schooling fish inhabiting the cool, medium depths of lakes. Feeding on many small invertebrates and some small fish, they, in turn, are preyed upon by other fishes, including many of our most prized sport species, such as the lake trout and landlocked salmon.

Smelt are caught by dip netting and winter ice fishing. Some of the best opportunities are in the Great Lakes, Lake Champlain, and Finger Lakes tributaries.

Mudminnow Family (Umbridae)

Central Mudminnow *(Umbra limi)*

This mudminnow is a small fish (3½ inches or less) with a rounded tail. It has vertical bars on its sides.

The central mudminnow is widely distributed in the Allegheny system and Lake Erie in western New York, in the Niagara River, along the coastal plain of Lake Ontario, and in the St. Lawrence River system. It is scattered through central New York, including the Finger Lakes and Oneida Lake. There are few records of it from northeastern New York.

Mudminnows spawn in April. Pairs move to shallow water, where the female deposits 200 to 2,000 adhesive eggs, which separately stick to vegetation. No parental care is given the eggs, which hatch in about 1 week, or the young. Dwelling in the muddy bottom waters of streams, ponds, and marshes, the adults are predominately plankton and insect eaters.

From an angler's viewpoint, the main value of mudminnows is as a food for game fish. Mudminnows are good aquarium fish because of their hardiness and tolerance of low dissolved oxygen levels in water.

Eastern Mudminnow *(Umbra pygmaea)*

This mudminnow is slightly smaller (3 inches or less) than the central mudminnow. It has the characteristic rounded tail, but it has longitudinal streaks rather than vertical bars. In New York this fish is common in the lower Hudson drainage and on southern Long Island.

Pike Family (Esocidae)

1

a. Gill cover entirely scaled; dark, vertical bar extending downward from eye

2

b. Gill cover with scales on upper half only; no dark, vertical bar extending downward from eye

3

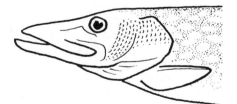

2

a. Sides and back marked with dark chain link or lacelike network; 14–16 branchiostegal rays on each side

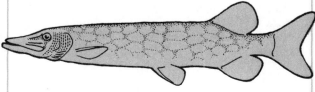

Chain Pickerel *(Esox niger)* p. 65

b. Sides and back marked with dark, wavy bands; 11–12 branchiostegal rays on each side

Grass Pickerel *(Esox vermiculatus)* p. 66

3

a. Cheek always entirely scaled; small, bean-shaped light spots on dark background; 5 or less sensory pores on each side of undersurface of lower jaw

Northern Pike *(Esox lucius)* p. 63

b. Lower half of cheek either wholly or partially without scales; body with dark vertical bars or spots (or with no marks) on light background; 6 or more sensory pores on each side of undersurface of lower jaw

Muskellunge *(Esox masquinongy)* p. 64

(Note: The norlunge or tiger muskellunge is a northern pike × muskellunge hybrid. It displays the cheek and gill-cover scale pattern of northern pike and the barred body markings of muskellunge. These fish have 5 to 8 sensory pores on each side of the undersurface of their lower jaw.)

Norlunge *(Esox lucius × Esox masquinongy)*
p. 65

Pike Family (Esocidae)

Four members of the pike family — chain pickerel, grass pickerel, northern pike, and muskellunge — are found in New York. In addition, a northern pike × muskellunge hybrid called "norlunge" or "tiger muskellunge" has been stocked in some waters. All of these fish share at least one well-known characteristic — voracious appetites. They feed heavily on fish, including their own kind; readily take artificial lures and all types of natural bait; fight hard when hooked; and often are found in shallow water. All this adds up to a popular sport fish.

Members of the pike family, like most other gamefish in New York, are currently managed with specific regulations on size, creel limits, and seasons for each species. Management policies require anglers to identify their catch correctly to apply proper regulations. Misidentification of fish prevents proper interpretation of fishing regulations and may cause unintentional violations of fish and wildlife laws.

Members of the pike family have been described as torpedo shaped, a good description considering their long, streamlined profile. Their general body shape and elongated, duckbill-shaped jaws are usually adequate clues to distinguish these fish from any others. Fins are soft rayed, lacking the stiff spines found in those of some other fishes, like sunfish and yellow perch. Median fins include the dorsal and anal, located opposite each other about three-quarters of the way back along the length of the fish near the tail. Members of the pike family do not have an adipose fin. Two sets of paired fins are present, the pelvic and pectoral fins. The pelvic fins are located midway on the fish's belly. The pectoral fins are positioned closer to the head.

Northern Pike *(Esox lucius)*

Northern pike inhabit most waters in northern New York and many large lakes and rivers of central and western New York. They are most abundant north of latitude 43°. They occur in and along the shores of Lakes Erie and Ontario, in the Finger Lakes region, and Oneida Lake. They are abundant in the St. Lawrence River system. They are rare in southeastern New York. These fish prefer large rivers and medium to large lakes. In lakes they stay in bays and straits, avoiding deep offshore water. They are loners, hunting in weedy or log-strewn shallows.

Pike spawn in early spring. They migrate to their spawning grounds during the night. Those living in streams move up them to spawning sites. Pike living in lakes move to spawning sites in the lake. The actual spawning takes place during daylight hours.

Adult northern pike feed almost exlusively on fish, with just about any fish (including young pike) being potential prey. They are not selective in their feeding habits, supplementing their fish diet with aquatic insects, leeches, crayfish, frogs, snakes, small muskrats, and ducklings. The northern pike is one of the most rapidly growing fish we have, averaging 2 to 4 pounds and 2 feet long. Often these fish reach the 20-pound class. They are one of our most important sport fish.

Muskellunge *(Esox masquinongy)*

The muskellunge (muskie) is the largest member of the pike family. Among New York's top muskie waters are the Niagara and St. Lawrence rivers, Chautauqua Lake, and Black Lake. Other waters such as the Allegheny, Delaware, and Susquehanna rivers, Lake Erie, and eastern Lake Ontario have muskellunge, but they are rare. They have been stocked in a few other lakes across the state.

Muskellunge spawn in the spring following the northern pike spawning period. Water temperatures between 48° and 56°F seem to be optimum for muskellunge spawning. Their age at first spawning varies between 3 and 6 years old. The males move to the spawning grounds first, the females following. Actual spawning takes place at night in shallow, muck-bottomed bays or coves, especially those with sunken stumps or logs. Eggs are distributed along several hundred feet of shoreline. No nests are built, and no parental care is given to eggs or young.

Muskies prefer habitat with clear, quiet water. Submerged weed beds interspersed with sunken stumps and logs are all components of ideal muskie habitat. They tend to move little, staying in their favorite lairs awaiting their prey, which consists of fish, frogs, snakes, small mammals, and aquatic birds. Muskies are sometimes cannibalistic to the extent of damaging their own populations. A rapidly growing fish, they reach sizes of several feet and can be in the 40–60-pound class. They are highly prized as sport fish; unfortunately, they are rather rare and few are caught.

The norlunge (or tiger muskellunge) is a northern pike × muskellunge hybrid. While this fish is stocked in some New York waters, it may occur naturally in waters inhabited by northern pike and muskellunge. Norlunge grow faster than either parent during their first year and at nearly the same rate as their parents during following years. They also exhibit greater vitality and experience a lower mortality rate than pure northern pike or muskellunge.

The New York State Department of Environmental Conservation has placed identification posters at access sites on waters they have stocked with norlunge to alert anglers to the presence of these fish.

Chain Pickerel *(Esox niger)*

The chain pickerel is widely distributed across most of the state, but is not common in many northern New York lakes. It is common in eastern New York State, including Long Island, westward through the Susquehanna drainage system and some of the Finger Lakes. It is not found in the Allegheny and Genesee river systems, and only isolated records exist from west of the Genesee River. Although chain pickerel may exceed 30 inches in length and weigh several pounds, the average fish is under 24 inches and weighs 1 to 2 pounds.

Chain pickerel spawn in swampy or marshy backwater areas of lakes and rivers soon after ice-out. No nest is built, and no parental care of eggs or young occurs. Eggs are dropped on the bottom, sticking to whatever they come in contact with. Small pickerel hatch within a couple of weeks. These young fish stay among the weeds close to shore throughout the summer. Young and adult pickerel feed primarily on other fish, although frogs and mice are consumed on occasion.

Grass Pickerel *(Esox vermiculatus)*

In New York, the grass pickerel inhabits sluggish streams and weedy bays of many waters across the state. Its distribution is spotty, and the probability of an angler encountering one is slight. This fish rarely reaches a length of 12 inches, with the average length being 9 inches or less.

The spawning behavior of grass pickerel is similar to that of the chain pickerel. These fish are carnivorous, feeding mainly on other fish, particularly minnows; aquatic insects, small crayfish, and frogs are also consumed. Because of its limited occurrence and small size, the grass pickerel is not an important sport fish.

Minnow Family (Cyprinidae)

1

a. Spines in anal and dorsal fins; more than 11 soft dorsal rays

2

b. No spines in anal and dorsal fins; less than 11 soft dorsal rays

3

2

a. Two barbels on each side of upper jaw

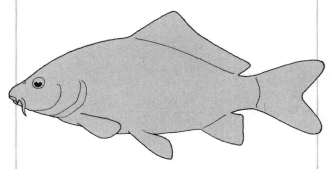

Carp *(Cyprinus carpio)* p. 81

b. No barbels on upper jaw

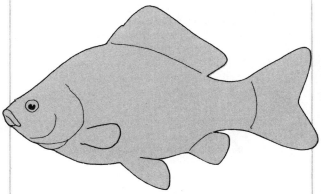

Goldfish *(Carassius auratus)* p. 79

3

a. Lower jaw with distinct inner cartilaginous ridge, separated by definite groove from lower lip; dark crossbar on both dorsal and anal fins

Detail of lower jaw

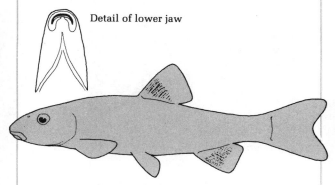

Stoneroller *(Campostoma anomalum)* p. 79

b. Lower jaw without distinct inner cartilaginous ridge separated from lower lip; lacks dark crossbar on both dorsal and anal fins

4

4

a. Upper lip separated from snout by complete groove

6

b. Upper lip connected to snout by a bridge of skin

5

5

a. Lower lip not modified by side lobes, continuous with central part of lip; short barbel at end of upper jaw; body flecked with darkened scales or speckled

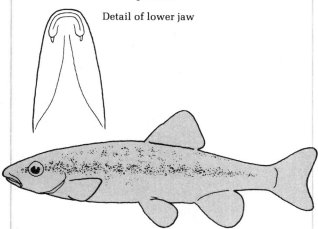

Detail of lower jaw

Dace *(Rhinichthys* spp.) p. 88

b. Lower lip modified with central tonguelike part flanked by fleshy side parts; no barbels present; body not speckled

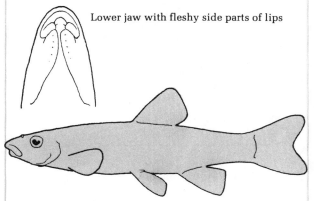

Lower jaw with fleshy side parts of lips

Cutlips Minnow *(Exoglossum maxillingua)* p. 82

6

a. Tiny barbel present (difficult to see) at or near corner of mouth

7

b. Barbel absent from mouth

11

7

a. Barbel a short distance in front of end of jaw

9

b. Barbel at end of jaw

8

8

a. Snout protruding only slightly past mouth

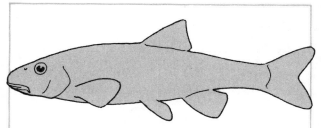

Chubs *(Nocomis* **spp.)** p. 84

b. Snout protruding considerably past mouth

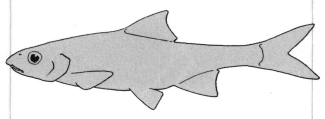

Chubs *(Hybopsis* **spp.)** p. 83

9 _____

a. Upper jaw extends back past nostril to or behind front of eye

10

b. Upper jaw ends under nostril, does not extend all the way back to eye

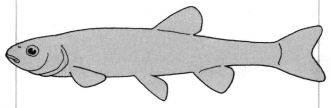

Pearl Dace *(Semotilus margarita)* p. 90

10

a. Black spot at anterior base of dorsal fin

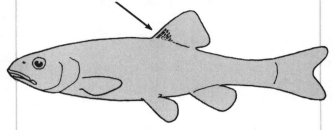

Creek Chub *(Semotilus atromaculatus)* p. 88

b. Lacks black spot at anterior base of dorsal fin

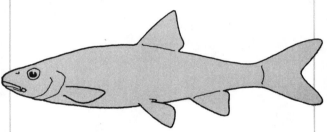

Fallfish *(Semotilus corporalis)* p. 89

11

a. Lateral line scales (or scales in body length) more than 45

12

b. Lateral line scales (or scales in body length) less than 45

13

12

a. Anal fin rays 10 or more; mouth small, jaw reaches only half the distance from front of mouth to eye; lateral line greatly decurved

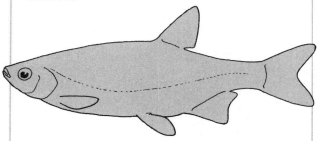

Golden Shiner *(Notemigonus crysoleucas)* p. 86

b. Anal fin rays less than 10; mouth large, jaw reaches back to eye; lateral line not greatly decurved

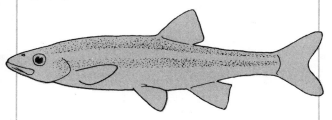

Redside or Rosyside Dace
(Clinostomus **spp.)** p. 80

13

a. First small dorsal fin ray separated from second, longer ray by fin membrane

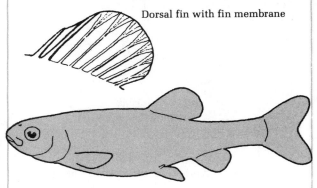

Dorsal fin with fin membrane

Fathead and Bluntnose Minnows
(Pimephales **spp.)** p. 87

b. First dorsal fin ray is closely attached to second fin ray, not separated by fin membrane

14

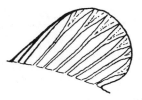

14

a. Intestine short (less than twice length of body) and s-shaped; abdomen lining (peritoneum) silvery or speckled

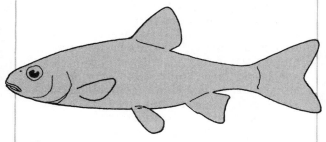

Shiners *(Notropis* **spp.)** p. 86

b. Intestine elongated (more than twice length of body); abdomen lining (peritoneum) black

Silvery and Brassy Minnows *(Hybognathus* **spp.)** p. 82

Minnow Family (Cyprinidae)

"Minnow" is often used to describe all small fish. Actually, it is the common name for a family of fishes that is by far the largest such family in New York. Some 48 species of minnows occur in the state; 5 of these are introduced species, among which carp and goldfish are best known. Other commonly encountered native species are creek chub, fallfish, chubs, stoneroller, golden shiner, common shiner, and various dace and minnows. Although many other fish are included in the minnow family, we will be concerned primarily with those named above.

Various kinds of minnow live in almost all freshwater (and some in brackish water) habitats. These range from headwater bogs, swamps, and springs to rivers, ponds, and lakes. It is possible to find a dozen different species of minnows in a single section of a moderately large stream.

The habits of the different minnows vary greatly. Some are found in schools all or a portion of the time, and others typically are found alone or associated with only a few others. Some kinds of minnows occur only in cold water; others are widely distributed in both cold and warmwater environments. Some, like the fallfish, prefer large streams, rivers, and lakes; others, like the pearl dace, usually live in small headwater tributaries.

The abundance of minnows may be attributed to three factors: they can occupy a great variety of habitats, most species require a relatively short period of time to reach breeding age, and a large number of minnows can occupy a small space and find sufficient food and shelter because of their small size.

Although the exotic carp and goldfish are very large minnows, most of our native species are small, seldom exceeding 4 inches. The creek chub, fallfish, and river chub are exceptions; these fish may reach a foot or more. The smaller minnows usually live only 3 or 4 years; larger species may live 7 to 10 years, and the carp may live somewhat longer.

The spawning season for New York's various minnows covers the period from early spring through midsummer, though each individual species has a more limited spawning time within this period. Minnows lay their eggs on or in the bottom, in algae or other aquatic plants, or the male may build and protect a nest.

Three general types of nests are constructed by minnows. First, there are nests consisting of piles of stones (carried by mouth to the nest); second, circular or cup-shaped depressions in or above riffles; and third, excavations under a stone, allowing the eggs to be attached to the underside of the stone.

Nests of more or less circular piles of stones are the easiest to identify, occurring either in fairly quiet waters or in riffles. These nests are built by the male, which carries the stones by mouth. Fallfish, chubs (*Hybopsis* spp.), and cutlips minnows build nests of this type. Fallfish nests have been measured as large as 6 feet in diameter and 3 feet high. Constructed with flat stones averaging 2 inches in diameter, fallfish nests usually have a keel-like crest, which may lie either crosswise or with the current. Chub nests average 2½ feet in diameter and are built up 6 to 12 inches. The cutlips minnow uses small pebbles to build nests about 10 to 18 inches in diameter.

Circular or cup-shaped depressions are excavated by the pit-digging minnows to receive the eggs. The stoneroller minnow, the creek chub, and the common shiner build this type of nest. Two to five male stonerollers work together on a single pit at the downstream end of a pool. They remove material by thrusting their snouts into the gravel and jerking their heads sideways. Stones are occasionally picked up in the mouth and carried upstream. Depressions are up to a foot in diameter. Males fight continually during the operation, even to the point of blinding one another with their breeding tubercles.

The creek chub chooses a spot over a sand and gravel bottom just above a riffle, then digs by forcing his head into the bottom and shaking vigorously. Sand and pebbles are placed upstream in a long ridge parallel to the course of the stream and varying from 1 to 18 feet in length. Subsequent digging covers the eggs.

The common shiner is the most versatile of the minnows; it may excavate a small depression in or above riffles, or it may spawn over the nest of other species, such as the creek chub, river chub, and cutlips.

The bluntnose minnow and fathead minnow fasten their eggs under stones in depressions they have dug.

Just before spawning season, males of many minnow species take on bright colors, including red and orange. In species that are nest builders, the males are usually larger and more brightly colored. They often develop nuptial or breeding tubercles on the body; these tubercles are usually more numerous on the head. The tubercles help to hold the female during spawning and serve as protection. After the spawning season the tubercles fall off and the males lose most or all of their bright colors.

Minnows are not considered game fish, though some larger ones (fallfish) may readily take a fly or worm and are fun to catch. Except for carp, they are seldom eaten. However, they are important in their role in aquatic ecosystems. Minnows of various sizes are eaten by the more popular game fish (and fish-eating birds); thus, they provide an important link in the food chain by converting certain small aquatic plants and animals (algae, insects, fish, etc.) into protein available to larger fish. Also, some naturalists believe that the presence of minnows relieves predation on the young of game fishes. On the other hand, minnows, especially larger ones, may compete with game fishes, particularly trout, for food and space. They also can harm reproduction of sport fish by consuming eggs and, in some cases, by preying upon the young fish.

Many of the minnow species are difficult to identify correctly, and one must exercise care in examining characteristics used to distinguish species.

Stoneroller *(Campostoma anomalum)*

The stoneroller is brownish and mottled in color; males are reddish with numerous tubercles during spring spawning season. The stoneroller reaches about 8 inches in length. In New York, this fish is found in clear brooks, creeks, and small rivers of the St. Lawrence River system, the southern tributaries of Lake Ontario, and the upper Susquehanna River system.

The stoneroller prefers the riffle areas of small to medium-sized streams of moderate gradient. This fish is a bottom feeder, living on insect larvae, small mollusks, and filamentous algae.

The stoneroller moves up small tributary streams to spawn in spring. One or several males make a nest, which is a pile of small stones about 1 foot in diameter, on clean gravel. The stones in this nest, some of which may be ½ inch in diameter, are carried and placed there by the males.

The stoneroller is of little sport value, although it can be caught on small wet flies or bits of worm. It is a good bait fish.

Goldfish *(Carassius auratus)*

Goldfish are similar in appearance to carp, but differ in two major respects: they lack barbels and a dark spot at the base of each scale. Goldfish have serrated spines, one each, on the dorsal and anal fins. All goldfish do not have the well-known bright gold color. Wild populations vary in color from the well-known gold to olive green or even creamy white. All of the basic color patterns may also be combined with black patches of varying size and shape. Goldfish do not reach the large size attained by carp; about 16–18 inches is maximum.

Goldfish are similar to carp in many respects other than appearance. Like carp, it is an introduced species, being a native of Asia. Goldfish are currently widespread throughout much of New York in waters suitable to their survival. They feed on aquatic plants and small aquatic animals, spawn in late spring, and seem to interbreed freely with carp. Like the carp, goldfish are generally considered a nuisance by fishermen.

Daces *(Clinostomus* spp.)

Minnows of this genus are usually about 3–4 inches long, have a broad, dark band along the lateral line, and have a pointed head with a large mouth. The redside dace *(Clinostomus elongatus)* is the most common member of this genus in New York. It is known from the Allegheny, Genesee, and upper Susquehanna river systems, from tributaries of Lake Erie, and from scattered populations in the Mohawk River system and nearby tributaries of the Hudson River. A concentration exists in the Oswegatchie and Black river systems but is not present in the St. Lawrence drainage. It is absent from Adirondack waters and the Delaware River system.

Typically found in headwater streams, the redside dace tends to avoid both very warm and extremely cold waters. In these small streams it prefers clear pools with stony bottoms. It occurs in schools that actively search for food during daylight hours.

As spawning season nears in mid-May, males move from pools to gravel spawning beds in or above a riffle (often the nest of a creek chub). Breeding males have a red band from the gills to the base of the dorsal fin. Both sexes develop breeding tubercles, although those of the female are smaller and fewer in number. At the time of actual spawning, the eggs are deposited among the gravel on the bottom of the nest.

Where dace occur in waters inhabited by trout, they compete for food. Both feed on aquatic insects; however, dace are also consumed by larger trout.

Carp *(Cyprinus carpio)*

Carp are the largest members of the minnow family. They are heavy-bodied fish and are usually bronze colored with large scales, each with a dark spot at the base. Their dorsal fin is long, containing one serrated spine in the front of the fin and more than 16 soft rays. They have two barbels on each side of the upper jaw.

First introduced into this country from Europe in 1876, the carp has since spread from coast to coast. They are widely distributed in New York. Carp tolerate most aquatic habitats, but prefer warm streams or lakes with muddy bottoms where they feed primarily on plankton, insects, and aquatic plants. Carp spawn in late spring. Their small, adhesive eggs are broadcast in shallow, weedy water.

Carp are considered a nuisance by most fishermen because of their mud-bottom feeding habits and their tendency to uproot plants while feeding. Feeding carp create considerable turbulence, which results in muddy water. Thus, their feeding areas are unsuitable for more popular gamefish. However, some people fish specifically for carp, which is understandable considering the sporty size some of these fish attain (over 50 pounds). They are also taken by bow and arrow fishermen.

In many parts of the world carp are considered a valuable human food resource. They have yet to acquire that reputation in the United States, and it is generally agreed that introduction of carp was a serious mistake. The carp story is an excellent example of the extreme care that must be exercised when one is tempted to "improve" upon the natural distribution of animal species.

Cutlips Minnow *(Exoglossum maxillingua)*

The cutlips minnow reaches an average total length of 3½–5½ inches. Its body is stout and dull silvery colored; its three-lobed lower jaw is distinctive. In New York, the cutlips is found from eastern Lake Ontario and the St. Lawrence drainage, including Lake Champlain, southward east of the Appalachian Mountains and including the Susquehanna River drainage. It is found in clear, fast-flowing streams where it prefers rocky pools rather than rapids.

Spawning takes place in May, June, and July over a gravel nest. The nests are circular, flat-topped mounds of stone 1–1½ feet in diameter and 3–6 inches deep. A male builds the nest by carrying stones in its mouth. The nests are built in areas of sufficient current to maintain a constant change in water. During spawning, the male may rework the nest, assuring that eggs are lodged among the stones.

The cutlips is a slow-moving, bottom-dwelling minnow. Its food consists mainly of aquatic insect larvae and other small aquatic animals. It is of little importance as a bait or sport fish.

Brassy Minnow *(Hybognathus hankinsoni)*
Silvery Minnow *(H. nuchalis)*

The brassy minnow reaches an average length of 2½ inches. In New York, the brassy minnow is found in cooler waters from Lake Champlain west across northern New York, including the St. Lawrence River area to and along Lake Ontario. This minnow is common in small streams and ponds, apparently preferring those with boggy, acid waters. It spawns in early spring in quiet water; little else is known of its spawning habits. It is primarily a plant eater, feeding heavily on algae. This minnow is also desirable for bait and is important as a forage fish for brook trout.

The silvery minnow averages about 3 inches long but may reach 5 inches. It seems to prefer large rivers. In New York it is found in the St. Lawrence, Mohawk, Hudson and Delaware rivers. Silvery minnows spawn in late April and early May. Breeding males may have some yellow on their sides and develop tubercles (the female occasionally develops tubercles, also). Their nonadhesive eggs are deposited in quiet, shallow backwaters, often on mud bottoms. These fish feed almost entirely on plant material. They are used for bait, but do not survive well in bait buckets.

Chubs *(Hybopsis* spp.)

Several species of chubs in the genus *Hybopsis* are found in New York; among these are the streamline chub (*Hybopsis dissimilis*), bigeye chub (*H. amblops*), and silver chub (*H. storeriana*). These fish vary in length, depending on species, the largest seldom exceeding 10 inches.

Bigeye Chub (*H. amblops*). The bigeye chub is usually 2 to 3½ inches long. In New York, it is widespread in the Allegheny River system and is found in a few tributaries of Lake Erie and western Lake Ontario east of the mouth of the Niagara River. It occurs in rivers and creeks of moderate current, preferring areas in streams with clean sand or fine gravel. It spawns from late May to June.

Streamline Chub (*H. dissimilis*). The streamline chub is a slender, silvery fish with a bluish lateral line on the side; this dark stripe sometimes appears to have about nine blotches along the side. Adults average 2–4 inches. In New York, it is restricted to the Allegheny River and its larger tributaries. It inhabits riffles and nearby pools.

Silver Chub *(H. storeriana).* This fish is silvery on the sides to milky white below. The bottom edge of the tail has two or three milky white rays, a distinctive characteristic in adults, which are slender with large fins. This fish may reach a length of 10 inches, but 4–7 inches is more common. In New York, silver chubs are found in Lake Erie and mouths of its tributaries, where it is often common, and possibly near the mouth of the Niagara River. This chub sometimes ranges into rather deep water. It spawns late in the season, from late May through June. It is used occasionally as a bait fish.

Chubs *(Nocomis* spp.)

Hornyhead Chub *(Nocomis biguttatus).* The hornyhead chub, also known as the redtail chub, is olive brown on the back, silvery on the sides, and creamy below. At the base of the tail, which is red, young fish have a distinct spot. This spot becomes less distinct with age. Adult males reach a length of about 6 to 9 inches (females are smaller). This fish found in tributaries of French Creek and the Niagara River, in scattered tributaries to southern Lake Ontario, and in a few streams in the Mohawk River system. It does not inhabit the Susquehanna, Delaware, or Hudson rivers. It lives in warm rivers and creeks, specifically in areas where aquatic plants occur.

Spawning occurs from late May through June. A nest is constructed by the male, which moves materials away from an area 1 to 2 feet in diameter, then piles pebbles in the cavity to a height of 6 inches. At spawning, eggs drop between the pebbles in the nest. Although the male hornyhead will drive off others of the same species, it tolerates other kinds of fish. Blacknose dace, common shiner, and stoneroller minnows, among others, use these nests for spawning. During the spawning period, males develop nuptial tubercles on the head from the snout to well behind the eyes.

The hornyhead feeds primarily on insect larvae, but eats other small animals, such as earthworms and crustaceans; some algae is also eaten. It is used occasionally as a bait fish.

River Chub *(N. micropogon).* The river chub has a slightly longer snout than the hornyhead, the tail is slate colored (never red), and the tail spot is absent or indistinct, even in young fish. The size is usually 4 to 8 inches, although males may reach 11 inches. This fish is found in warm streams in western New York, including the Lake Ontario drainage, and in the Susquehanna River system. It does not occur in the Delaware, Hudson, or Mohawk river systems or in streams north and east of the latter. It avoids the cooler headwater streams and is associated with clear streams with a gravel bottom.

The river chub spawns in late May and June. During the spawning period the male's head swells greatly and develops nuptial tubercles on the head, from the snout back to the area between the eyes. The nest is a prominent heap of pebbles piled by the male. Nests which may exceed 2 feet in diameter and 1 foot high are typically located in the shallow parts of large pools, just ahead of the riffles. Other fishes, like the common shiner, spawn over these nests.

The river chub feeds primarily at or near the bottom on insects, crustaceans, and other small animals, as well as algae. It will take a bait and may be caught by an angler using worms. The river chub is often found in bass streams where young are probably a forage for large game fish. River chubs are good bait fish.

Golden Shiner *(Notemigonus crysoleucas)*

The golden shiner is present throughout New York. Young golden shiners are silvery with a dusky band along the side. This band fades with age as the fish takes on a golden color. Golden shiners live in clear, weedy, quiet, shallow sections of lakes, ponds, and occasionally rivers (such as the St. Lawrence River). Both young and adult fish show schooling behavior. Golden shiners spawn over an extended period from May to July. Females deposit adhesive eggs over filamentous algae and submerged weed beds. After spawning, the eggs are abandoned. Adults are usually less than 6 inches long.

Golden shiners feed on planktonic crustaceans, aquatic insects, and algae. They are important forage fish for more popular game fish and are often stocked in farm ponds in combination with largemouth bass. Golden shiners are used extensively as bait.

Common Shiner *(Notropis cornutus)*

Common shiners average about 2½ to 4 inches long; some reach 8 inches. Their color is basically silvery with a dusky back. In comparison with similar species, the head, eyes, and mouth of the common shiner seem noticeably large. Widely distributed in New York, this fish is present in all drainages and in most habitats, but is less common in lakes. It inhabits both warm and coldwater streams; in the latter, it may be found in the same waters as trout.

Common shiners spawn in spring. Gravel in riffles is often used for spawning, but they commonly spawn over the nest of a creek chub, river chub, or fallfish; some males excavate their own small nests. They hybridize regularly with other species of minnow that spawn at the same time over the nest.

The common shiner feeds at or just below the water surface primarily on insects. Because it is common and readily caught, it is a popular bait minnow; it is an important forage fish for game fish. It takes a fly readily and is often caught by beginning fly fishermen.

Bluntnose Minnow *(Pimephales notatus)*

The bluntnose minnow is a small minnow, 2–3 inches long, 4 inches being maximum. This fish has a prominent dark lateral stripe that extends from the tip of the snout back almost to the base of the tail; a dark spot is located at the base of the tail. The bluntnose minnow occurs in small creeks, rivers, or lakes throughout New York, with the exception of the Susquehanna River system (although it may have been released in these waters). Spawning extends through most of the summer, and spawning habits are similar to those of the fathead minnow. Eggs are deposited on the underside of underwater objects and are guarded by the male. The food of this fish is aquatic insects, animal plankton, and aquatic vegetation. Unlike the fathead, bluntnose minnows often occur in the same waters as game fish and are important forage for them. Although not as popular as the fathead minnow, the bluntnose is also raised as a bait fish.

Fathead Minnow *(Pimephales promelas)*

This minnow reaches an average length of 2–2½ inches, 3–3½ inches being the maximum. The fathead minnow occurs throughout northern and western New York, but is absent from the Susquehanna River system east (although it may have been released in waters of this area). It is most common in mud-bottomed ponds and streams. Males and females have a dark lateral band across the dorsal fin. Breeding males develop a conspicuous gray pad of spongy tubercles on the back, between the head and the dorsal fin, and two rows of tubercles across the snout. During spawning, the upper sides of the body usually become dark with the lower sides rather silvery white. Also, two light vertical bars sometimes develop, one behind the head and the other beneath the dorsal fin. The prolonged spawning period of this fish occurs from the time the water reaches 67°–68° F through most of the summer. With active encouragement from the male, the female deposits the eggs on the underside of boards, logs, rocks, or other underwater objects. Once the eggs are deposited and fertilized, the male drives the female away and guards the nest. Aquatic insects, plant material, and animal plankton are the main foods of this fish. The fathead minnow is one of the hardiest bait fish and is widely raised for this purpose.

Daces *(Rhinichthys* spp.)

Two common species of dace are the blacknose dace *(R. atratulus)* and longnose dace *(R. cataractae)*. Dace are small fish (2–3 inches). Both species prefer small streams and are often found in the same stream. The longnose dace sometimes is found living in turbulent waters. Dace occur throughout New York.

From late spring to early summer, dace spawn in riffles over gravel and rubble where both the male and female construct a nest of small pebbles. After spawning, little parental care is given the eggs.

Dace feed on all types of aquatic insect larvae, worms, and algae. They are sometimes used as bait and are quite hardy.

Creek Chub *(Semotilus atromaculatus)*

The creek chub is a medium-sized minnow, reaching lengths of 8–10 inches. Its color is black or bluish above and silvery below. It has a single, small barbel in the corner of each jaw. Sometimes the barbel is hidden between the maxillary and premaxillary. Adult fish are most easily identified by the dark spot at the base of the dorsal fin.

In New York, the creek chub is found in creeks of all drainages outside of Long Island. It is both a forage fish for larger predacious sport fish and a competitor with them for aquatic insect and crustacean food forms. During the spring spawning season, male creek chubs take on a bright, rosy coloration and develop at least four large tubercles on each side of their heads. The breeding tubercles are the basis for one of the local common names of the creek chub, "horned dace." The male creek chub builds and carefully guards a mound of small stones in which the eggs are deposited. In New York, creek chubs often inhabit trout streams. Small creek chubs are used as bait.

Fallfish *(Semotilus corporalis)*

Fallfish, often called chubs or whitefish in New York, are the largest of our native minnows; they reach a length of 12 inches or more and a weight of up to 2 pounds. Closely resembling the creek chub, they lack the dark spot at the base of the dorsal fin. Their color is basically silvery with a dark back. Fallfish prefer rivers and lakes and do not usually occur in headwater streams. In New York, they are found east and northeast of the upper Susquehanna River system. They are common in the Delaware and Susquehanna systems. Few are present in the Adirondacks, and they are generally absent in the higher elevations.

Fallfish spawn in the spring. Like the creek chub, males acquire a rosy coloration and develop tubercles during the spawning period. Males build nests of small stones in shallow areas of a lake or in quiet pools in streams. These nests of stones may be several feet in diameter and up to 2 feet high.

Fallfish eat aquatic insects for the greatest part of their diet. Small fallfish (sometimes used as bait) are eaten by larger sport fish, but the large fallfish compete with trout for aquatic insects. They are of little value as food and of minimal importance for sport fishing, although they will strike readily on both natural and artificial baits.

Pearl Dace *(Semotilus margarita)*

The pearl dace is a stout-bodied minnow that reaches lengths of up to 6 inches, 3—4 inches being average. It is dusky mottled on the upper sides and silvery on the lower sides. During the breeding season, males have a pink to red-tinted stripe along their lower sides, and the upper sides of the pectoral fins bear paired rows of small, sharp tubercles. In New York, the northern subspecies of pearl dace is limited to the Adirondacks and tributaries of southeastern Lake Ontario. The southern subspecies of pearl dace is common in the Allegheny, Susquehanna, and Genesee river systems. Scattered populations through mid—New York may represent intergrades between the two subspecies. This fish can be found in the cool, boggy waters of lakes and ponds and in the cold headwater streams often associated with trout. It spawns in streams from late spring to early summer. No nest is built, but the small spawning area is guarded by the male. Pearl dace are forage fish for larger sport fishes in some waters. They feed on aquatic insects, free-floating animal plankton, and a variety of other small aquatic organisms.

Sucker Family (Catostomidae)

1

a. Dorsal fin with long base (more than 20 rays); first 4–7 rays of dorsal fin greatly elongated to make a pointed or rounded lobe at least 2 times as high as last half of fin; dorsal fin base longer than half the distance from origin of dorsal fin to base of tail

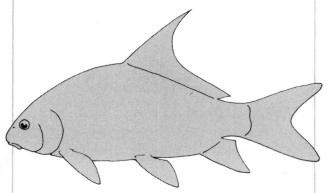

Quillback *(Carpiodes cyprinus)* p. 95

b. Dorsal fin with short base (fewer than 20 rays); no pronounced pointed or rounded lobe on front of dorsal fin; dorsal fin base shorter than half the distance from origin of dorsal fin to base of tail

2

2

a. Lateral line absent or incomplete in adults; greatest body depth equal to or greater than 1/3 length of body from tip of snout to base of tail; sides with wide, longitudinal black band which may break up into blotches in large specimens (over 6 inches)

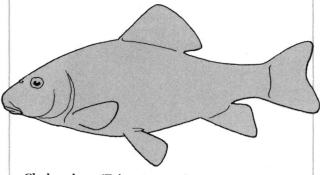

Chubsuckers *(Erimyzon* spp.) p. 96

b. Lateral line complete in adults; greatest body depth less than 1/3 length of body from tip of snout to base of tail

3

3

a. Scales not crowded and of uniform size from head to tail

4

b. Scales crowded toward front of body and larger toward tail

5

4

a. No dark patches on sides; top of head between eyes rounded (convex); lower fins, especially tail, are reddish in color

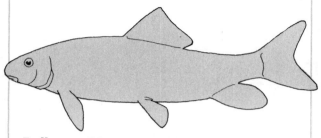

Redhorses *(Moxostoma* **spp.)** p. 97

b. Dark blotches on sides; depression in top of head between eyes (concave); lower fins not reddish

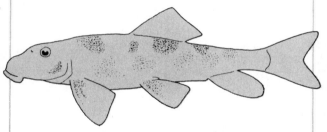

Hogsuckers *(Hypentelium* **spp.)** p. 96

5

a. Snout blunt and rounded; upper lip thinner than lower lip; scales large, fewer than 80 in lateral line

White Sucker *(Catostomus commersoni)* p. 95

b. Snout pointed, extends forward considerably beyond mouth; upper and lower lips similar in thickness; scales small, more than 80 in lateral line

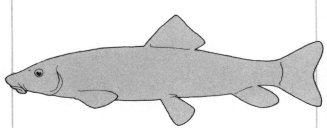

Longnose Sucker *(Catostomus catostomus)* p. 95

Sucker Family (Catostomidae)

The sucker family contains many species and is widely distributed throughout the United States. Suckers are omnivorous, feeding on both animal and plant material on lake and stream bottoms. All suckers are spring spawners, some ascending streams in vast numbers. They spawn in groups over shallow, swift water. The fertilized eggs sink to the bottom, are entrapped in the spaces between gravel or adhere to gravel and are given no parental care. They are important as forage for sport fish and are occasionally sought and eaten by people.

Quillback *(Carpiodes cyprinus)*

Quillbacks are a large, deep-bodied sucker with a humpback appearance. They average 10–15 inches long and 4–6 pounds at maturity. In New York, they occur in Lake Erie and the Allegheny River.

Longnose Sucker *(Catostomus catostomus)*

The longnose sucker has a long, round, torpedo-shaped body, usually 12–14 inches long and weighing about 1½ pounds. As its name implies, it is characterized by a long snout.

This fish is distributed north of latitude 42° in eastern New York. It occurs in tributaries of the Hudson and Mohawk rivers and in the Adirondacks. It is also found in the St. Lawrence River, Lake Ontario, and Owasco Lake. Deep, cold water is the preferred habitat of this fish. Of little angling value, the longnose sucker is sometimes caught with worms as bait or speared on its spawning run; its flesh is edible. This species is important as forage for larger game fish.

White Sucker *(Catostomus commersoni)*

White suckers are usually about 10–20 inches long and weigh 1–2 pounds, some unusual specimens weighing as much as 8 pounds. Their color is olive brown, and they have a cylindrical shape.

The white sucker is widely distributed in all drainage systems in New York State. It is found in almost any water condition —lakes and streams, muddy or clear water, polluted or otherwise. The white sucker prefers large streams and the bottoms of lakes and reservoirs.

These fish feed on a variety of organisms occurring in the mud and ooze of stream and lake bottoms. They are not highly regarded as food fish, although their flesh is sweet and firm when taken from cold waters. Like most other suckers, their primary value is as forage for more desirable game fish. Young white suckers are often used as bait.

Creek Chubsucker *(Erimyzon oblongus)*

Lake Chubsucker *(Erimyzon sucetta)*

Chubsuckers are small fish, usually 10 inches or less, and greenish bronze colored. Their lips are not as fleshy as those of the white sucker.

Creek chubsuckers are widely distributed in eastern New York from the Susquehanna River system eastward, including northeast Lake Ontario and tributaries. Lake chubsuckers in New York are found in a few scattered locations along Lake Ontario and in one tributary of Lake Erie.

Chubsuckers usually spawn in small tributary streams in early spring. The male cleans a nest, or the nonadhesive eggs are scattered.

Chubsuckers prefer low-turbidity lakes and rivers. Like other members of the sucker family, chubsuckers are bottom feeders. Their diet is mostly insect larvae, aquatic plants, and tiny crustaceans. Neither species is of any importance to commercial or recreational fisheries in New York.

Hogsucker *(Hypentelium nigricans)*

The hogsucker has a long, slender body with a head broader than the rest of the body. The head is slightly concave between the eyes. Four dark bars mottle its brown body, allowing it to blend easily with stony stream bottoms. Average length of this fish is 6–12 inches.

This fish is widely distributed in western New York, including the Finger Lakes region. In the Mohawk–Hudson system, its distribution is limited to the middle Hudson. It occurs in tributaries of Lake Erie and Lake Ontario. It is not found north of latitude 44°.

The hogsucker resides in the riffles of clear, shallow streams where it feeds by sucking ooze off the top of stones. It also uses its long snout and bony head to push aside rocks on the stream bottom. Then, using its paired fins to hold its position in the current, it feeds on the insects and other organisms in the mud from beneath the rocks. Other fish may benefit by feeding on the insects washed past the foraging hogsucker.

Hogsuckers are of no sport fishing value, and they are not palatable. They are important in their role of liberating food for other, more desirable species and as forage for larger game fish.

Redhorses (*Moxostoma* spp.)

Several species of redhorse are found in New York — silver, black, golden, greater, and shorthead — although none is particularly common. The shorthead redhorse is probably the most common and is certainly the most widespread species of redhorse in New York State.

Generally, redhorses have a dark back and silvery sides, giving a bronze or copper reflection. These fish usually have paired fins with red, orange, or copper tint; some species also have red to orange dorsal, anal, and tail fins. They range in average size from 10 to 18 inches and from 1 to several pounds.

As with other suckers, redhorses spawn in spring. They are bottom feeders, and probably their greatest importance is as food for game fish. They are used as food in the spring by some people.

Silver Redhorse *(Moxostoma anisurum).* This fish is found in larger streams in the Allegheny and French Creek drainages of western New York, tributaries of Lake Erie, a few tributaries of western Lake Ontario, tributaries of the St. Lawrence River, and the Lake George region.

Black Redhorse *(Moxostoma duquesnei).* The distribution of this fish is limited to western New York in the Allegheny system, tributaries of Lake Erie, and the lower Genesee River, a tributary of Lake Ontario.

Golden Redhorse *(Moxostoma erythrurum).* This is a western species that in New York is found in the Allegheny system, tributaries of Lake Erie, and tributaries of western Lake Ontario, including the Genesee River.

Shorthead Redhorse *(Moxostoma macrolepidotum).* The most common redhorse in New York, the shorthead redhorse prefers large lakes and streams. It is widely distributed in New York from Lake Erie along Lake Ontario, the Genesee River, Cayuga Lake, St. Lawrence River, eastern Mohawk River, and the upper Delaware River. A few are recorded from northeast New York.

Greater Redhorse *(Moxostoma valenciennesi).* The distribution of this fish in New York is limited to several tributaries of Lake Ontario and the St. Lawrence River.

Catfish Family (Ictaluridae)

1

a. Tail fin moderately to deeply forked

2

b. Tail fin rounded, squared, or only slightly forked

3

2

a. Tail fin deeply forked, with lobes of tail fin pointed; small, irregular black spots on sides

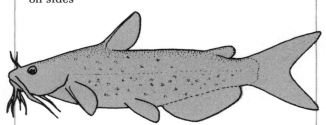

Channel Catfish _(Ictalurus punctatus)_ p. 103

b. Tail fin moderately forked, with lobes of tail fin rounded; no black spots on sides

White Catfish _(Ictalurus catus)_ p. 103

3

a. Adipose fin free, not connected to tail fin

4

b. Adipose fin not free, connected to tail fin or separated by a slight or incomplete notch

Madtoms and Stonecat *(Noturus* **spp.)** p. 104

4

a. Tail fin rounded; barbels on the chin are white

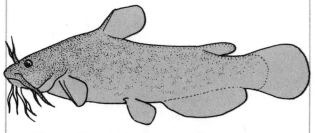

Yellow Bullhead *(Ictalurus natalis)* p. 105

b. Tail fin squared or slightly forked; barbels on the chin are gray to black

5

5

a. Rear edge of pectoral spine strongly serrated, with saw-toothed appearance (when spine held between thumb and forefinger, serrations provide good grip against slipping); no light bar at base of tail fin; fin membranes not black; lower sides often with mottled appearance

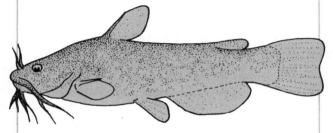

Brown Bullhead *(Ictalurus nebulosus)* p. 105

b. Rear edge of pectoral spine not strongly serrated (when spine held between thumb and forefinger, serrations provide little resistance against slipping); light bar at base of tail fin; fin membranes black; lower sides not with mottled appearance

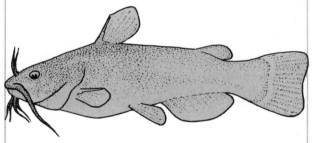

Black Bullhead *(Ictalurus melas)* p. 105

Catfish Family (Ictaluridae)

Five members of the catfish family are among New York's food and sport fish: brown bullhead, black bullhead, yellow bullhead, white catfish, and channel catfish. In addition, the stonecat and three species of madtom occur in New York, but since these small fish are not used for food or sport, they will be identified only as a group. Current New York fishing regulations require anglers to differentiate channel and white catfish from the bullheads. Misidentification of these fish prevents proper interpretation of these regulations and may cause unintentional violations of fish and wildlife laws.

Catfish have eight sensory barbels, or "whiskers", around the mouth; four on the chin, two on the snout, and one on each corner of the mouth. They have three median fins: anal, adipose, and dorsal. The anal fin has a long base and is located on the underside of the fish. The dorsal fin is located on the back and has a single sharp spine in the front part. The adipose fin is a small, fatty fin situated between the dorsal fin and the tail. Two sets of paired fins, the pelvic and pectoral fins, are also present. Both pectoral fins have a single spine in the front section of the fin. The tail may be squared or deeply forked, depending on the particular kind of catfish. None of the catfishes have scales.

Members of the catfish family in the U. S. were originally distributed in most states east of the Rocky Mountains, but various species have been widely introduced into western states where they did not occur naturally. Mature individuals among the species range in size from several pounds for the channel catfish to only a few ounces for the tiny madtoms. Large catfish are good food fish, and the madtoms and stonecat are good bass bait.

Catfishes are generally warmwater fish. They frequently inhabit mud-bottomed streams, ponds, and lakes, although channel catfish and madtoms prefer swift, cool streams. Catfishes can withstand water with low oxygen levels and considerable pollution. These fish are nocturnal, feeding most actively at night primarily on insects, crustacea, and fish; plant matter is consumed, also. The sensory barbels are used to locate food at night.

Catfishes spawn in late spring or early summer when the water temperature reaches about 70°F. The male usually excavates a saucer-shaped depression for a nest. Channel catfish dig tunnels in streambanks or under logs for their nests. Eggs hatch in about one week. After spawning, the male protects the eggs and schooling young for as much as two weeks after hatching. You may have observed one of these groups of young accompanied by their paternal babysitter since they are often very close to shore.

Channel Catfish *(Ictalurus punctatus)*

In New York, the channel catfish is found in Lake Erie, Lake Ontario, Lake Champlain, Oneida Lake, and their larger tributaries and in the Finger Lakes, the Canal System, the St. Lawrence drainage, and the Niagara River. This fish is found in lakes and streams with gravelly or stony bottoms more often than in those with mud bottoms.

Channel catfish in New York usually weigh 2–4 pounds and may occasionally exceed this. However, our channel cats do not reach the weights of 40–50 pounds recorded for the southeastern states where growing seasons are longer and living conditions more favorable.

White Catfish *(Ictalurus catus)*

In New York, white catfish occur in the Hudson River where they are common below Albany and may also be found in the lower sections of some larger tributaries as they join the lower Hudson. This fish reaches a larger size than bullheads, but is not as large as the channel catfish.

Madtoms and Stonecat
(*Noturus* spp.)

Madtoms and the stonecat are the smallest members of the catfish family. Madtoms average 2 to 3 inches in length, and stonecats average 6 to 8 inches, with a maximum length of 12 inches. Stonecats differ from madtoms by having a protruding upper jaw and a slight notch in their tail.

The stonecat (*Noturus flavus*) is common in the Allegheny system and tributaries of Lake Erie; it occurs along the coastal plain of Lake Ontario and the St. Lawrence River system; and it is scattered through the Mohawk system. The tadpole madtom (*Noturus gyrinus*) is widely distributed along the Lake Ontario coastal plain including the Genesee River, Cayuga Lake, and upper St. Lawrence River. Its range extends eastward through Oneida Lake and the Mohawk River. There are scattered records from the lower Hudson and the Delaware River. The margined madtom (*Noturus insignis*) is common throughout the Susquehanna and Delaware drainages. It has been reported from a few isolated locations in central New York and in the lower Hudson. The brindled madtom (*Noturus miurus*) is found in the Allegheny drainage, along the western coastal plain of Lake Ontario, and in Oneida Lake.

Both madtoms and stonecats are usually found under or among rocks in the swift water of streams, especially in riffle areas. They also are found in weedy water near shore or in the mud at the mouth of streams.

These fish have poison glands at the bases of their pectoral and dorsal fin spines. If the spines should prick your skin, the poison runs down the spine and into the wound, resulting in a painful sensation similar to a wasp sting. Stonecats and madtoms are tenacious of life and make good bass bait. They are of no real food or sport value, but are interesting members of the catfish family.

Yellow Bullhead *(Ictalurus natalis)*

In New York, the yellow bullhead is less common than the brown bullhead. The yellow bullhead occurs in Findley Lake, extreme western tributaries of Lake Erie, Genesee River system, bays and tributaries along Lake Ontario's southern and eastern shores, Oneida Lake, the Mohawk and mid–Hudson River System, in tributaries of the lower Hudson River, and in the St. Lawrence River. This fish prefers sluggish creeks, bays, and lakes; its length is 7 to 11 inches, though it may reach lengths exceeding 13 inches under favorable conditions.

Brown Bullhead *(Ictalurus nebulosus)*

The brown bullhead, the most common member of the catfish family in New York, is distributed throughout the state and is the only catfish present in the fresh waters of Long Island and Staten Island. Its average length is 9–13 inches, and average weight is about ½ pound. Populations of small brown bullheads occur in cool Adirondack lakes, and large individuals (several pounds) are usually found in large rivers and lakes downstate.

Black Bullhead *(Ictalurus melas)*

Not nearly as common as the brown bullhead in New York, black bullhead are restricted to the upper Genesee River drainage, a few locations in the Lake Ontario drainage, and in tributaries of the St. Lawrence River. The black, like the brown and yellow bullhead, is found in silty water and soft mud bottoms and avoids cold, clear water. This is the smallest of the bullheads found in New York, seldom reaching 12 inches in length. Its small size and restricted distribution make it less popular than the brown or yellow bullheads, although it is a good food fish.

Trout-perch Family (Percopsidae)

Trout-perch (Percopsis omiscomaycus)

As the name implies, the trout-perch superficially resembles both a trout and a perch. This fish has an adipose fin (a trout characteristic), but its general body configuration is more like that of a perch or young walleye. Trout-perch reach a maximum length of 6 to 8 inches, specimens 3 to 5 inches being most common.

Trout-perch are found in Lake Erie, Lake Ontario, and the St. Lawrence River. It is most common in western New York and the Allegheny and Genesee river systems. It also occurs in Cayuga, Seneca, and Oneida lakes, and in the Mohawk River system. There are scattered records in tributaries of the Hudson River and a few records for the extreme northeastern part of the state.

Trout-perch spawn from late May to late June, usually on the sand and gravel bottoms of tributary streams, but occasionally on sandbars in lakes. Females release between 200 and 800 eggs at spawning. It is believed that large females and most males die after spawning, although a few females and very few males live to spawn twice.

Adult trout-perch generally stay in water of medium depth during the day, but they move into shallow, near-shore areas at night. They feed on aquatic insects and small crustaceans, and, in turn, they are an important food for many sport and commercial fish. Trout-perch are used as a bait fish by lake trout fishermen, but are not sufficiently hardy to survive well in a bait bucket. Fishermen dipping for smelt in the spring frequently encounter the trout-perch.

Cod Family (Gadidae)

Burbot *(Lota lota)*

The burbot (also called ling, lawyer, or cusk) is North America's only freshwater member of the cod family. A burbot's body is elongate. It has a small barbel on each anterior nostril and one on the middle of the chin. It has two dorsal fins, the first of which is short. Both the second dorsal fin and the anal fin are long. The burbot's heavy skin is dark olive with chainlike blackish or yellowish markings on the sides.

Burbot occur in Lake Erie, the Allegheny drainage, lakes of Central New York, Lake Ontario, tributaries of the St. Lawrence River, and Oneida Lake, and scattered records are also noted for the eastern branch of the Susquehanna River system. They are also present in tributaries of Lake George.

Burbot spawn in February under ice. They spawn in groups over sand or gravel bottoms in 1 to 4 feet of water. No nest is built, and no care is given the young. Adults prefer deep, cold water.

Burbot in the Great Lakes are usually about 1 to 5 pounds. This carnivorous fish feeds primarily on other fish. It is usually regarded as an undesirable species because it competes with some of our important coldwater sport fish for food. Although generally not considered important by fishermen as food, some people think highly of the eating qualities of its delicately flavored flesh.

Killifish Family (Cyprinodontidae)

Banded Killifish *(Fundulus diaphanus)*

The banded killifish is the only freshwater member of the killifish family present in New York. These little fish are found in the quiet waters of lakes, ponds, rivers, and estuaries.

The banded killifish is a small (2–4 inches), slender fish with a head that is somewhat flattened on top and a small mouth adapted to surface feeding. The tail is nearly square or slightly convex or rounded. Olive green on the back and white on the lower side and belly, it has numerous light and dark vertical bars along its sides.

Banded killifish are abundant on Long Island and in the Hudson River and St. Lawrence River drainages. They are fairly common in Lake Ontario and its tributaries, including the Finger Lakes and Oneida Lake. Scattered records elsewhere suggest that its distribution actually covers the state.

Stickleback Family (Gasterosteidae)

Fourspine Stickleback *(Apeltes quadracus)*
Brook Stickleback *(Culaea inconstans)*
Threespine Stickleback *(Gasterosteus aculeatus)*
Ninespine Stickleback *(Pungitius pungitius)*

Sticklebacks are small fish (2–4 inches) characterized by a row of free dorsal spines in front of the dorsal fin combined with the absence of scales. Four species of sticklebacks occur in New York. Threespine and ninespine sticklebacks are commonly found in both fresh and salt water. In fresh water, they are primarily inhabitants of shores along large lakes and rivers. The threespine stickleback is found along the shore of Lake Ontario, in the St. Lawrence River, and on Long Island. The ninespine stickleback is common on Long Island, and is recorded from Keuka and Canandaigua lakes, with a few records from Lake Ontario. The fourspine stickleback is most common on Long Island and in the lower Hudson River to Albany. The fourth New York member of the stickleback family, found only in fresh water, is the brook stickleback, which has five spines. It is widely distributed in Lake Erie and in the Allegheny and Genesee river systems. It occurs along Lake Ontario in central New York, near eastern Lake Ontario, and in tributaries of the St. Lawrence River system. In central New York it extends through Oneida Lake and in the Mohawk system to tributaries of the Hudson River. There are some records from extreme northeast New York.

Male sticklebacks build elaborate, golf ball-sized nests. Grasses and fibers are cemented together with a secretion from their body. The hollow, fibrous nest has an entrance hole and an exit hole for placement of the eggs inside. The male aggressively guards the nest and eggs against all intruders.

Sticklebacks are not important forage fish and, consequently, of little value as bait. They feed on tiny aquatic animals.

Temperate Bass Family (Percichthyidae)

1

a. Dorsal fins separate at base; soft anal rays 9 to 13; lower jaw slightly to strongly projecting; sides with dark stripes.

2

b. Dorsal fins slightly joined by thin membranes at base; soft anal rays 8 to 10; upper and lower jaws about equal length; sides without dark stripes

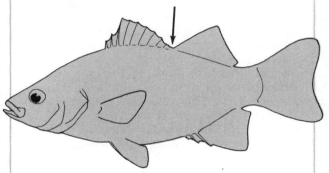

White Perch *(Morone americana)* p. 112

2

a. Depth of body more than 1/3 length of body from snout to base of tail; soft anal rays 12 or 13; longest anal spine is about 1/2 length of longest soft ray of anal fin; 5 to 7 dark stripes on side

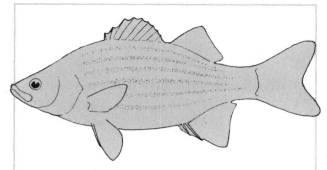

White Bass *(Morone chrysops)* p. 112

b. Depth of body less than 1/3 length of body from snout to base of tail; soft anal rays 9 to 11; longest anal spine less than 1/2 the length of longest soft ray of anal fin; 7 to 8 dark stripes on side

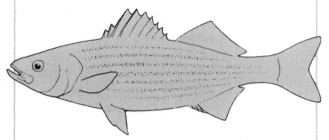

Striped Bass *(Morone saxatilis)* p. 113

Temperate Basses (Percichthyidae)

Three members of the temperate bass family live in the fresh waters of New York. The white bass and white perch are found in many bodies of fresh water; the striped bass is generally a marine fish ascending freshwater streams to spawn. Temperate basses resemble the largemouth and smallmouth bass in gross appearance, but they can be easily distinguished by the presence of two dorsal fins, except for the white perch, which has the spiny and soft-rayed dorsal fins slightly joined by a thin membrane. They are all spring spawners.

White Perch *(Morone americana)*

A white perch superficially resembles a striped bass, but like the white bass, it is chunkier and has a slightly humpback appearance. Its two dorsal fins are not completely separated, but are deeply notched. Ventral fins each are armed with one stout spine. A white perch usually lacks stripes; its back is dark and sides are pale silvery green, fading to a pale silvery white belly.

In New York, white perch are common on Long Island and in the lower Hudson River, including the lower Mohawk River. They are also present in Oneida Lake, Lake Ontario, the Seneca and Niagara rivers, and in a few locations in north central New York.

White perch are prolific breeders. In spring, schools crowd into tributary streams or along gravelly shoal areas in lakes where, without pairing off, females expel from 20,000 to 300,000 sticky eggs, which adhere to most anything, as males release sperm. The eggs are then abandoned. This seemingly haphazard reproduction strategy produces one of the highest hatching rates in fish. These fish are also long-lived.

White perch school in large numbers, keeping to deep water during the day and moving inshore at night. An angler who is fortunate enough to locate a school of feeding white perch is in for some fast and furious action. Though not large, the 8- to 10-inch, ¾- to 1-pound fish are scrappy fighters on light tackle. They are palatable, but not among the most popular panfishes in New York.

White Bass *(Morone chrysops)*

The moderately compressed body and small head of the white bass make this fish appear deep for its length. In New York, white bass average 10–12 inches long and about ½ pound.

White bass are exclusively freshwater fish that prefer large, clear lakes, but are found in some large streams and rivers. Lakes in excess of 300 acres and with extensive portions of water 10 feet deep are best. White bass often travel in large schools as they feed near the surface. In New York, white bass are present in lakes Ontario and Erie, in Cayuga, Seneca, and Oneida lakes; and in the St. Lawrence, Niagara, and Seneca rivers.

White bass move to tributary streams or shoals to spawn in the spring. The female deposits between 250,000 and 1 million heavy, adhesive eggs either near the surface or midwater in 6–7 feet of water. The eggs sink to the bottom where they stick to gravel, boulders, or vegetation. No parental care is given eggs or young, which hatch in about 2 days.

White bass feed primarily on other fish and insects. They are considered a good sport fish, being hard fighters and good eating.

Striped Bass *(Morone saxatilis)*

Striped bass are anadromous and can be found in fresh or brackish water, preferring estuarine and bay areas. In New York, the primary areas in which stripers are found are Long Island, the Hudson River, and the lower Mohawk River.

Striped bass ascend streams in late spring when the water temperature is between 55° and 65°F. Spawning females, accompanied by several males, release from 14,000 to 4½ million eggs (depending on the female's size). In the Hudson River, they spawn near the surface over a sand or gravel bottom in an area with a substantial current. The semibuoyant eggs usually drift downstream for a considerable distance, hatching in 2–3 days.

Striped bass vary considerably in length. A 125-pound fish, estimated to be 6 feet long, was caught in North Carolina. Fifty-pound stripers are rare, and most of those caught in New York are probably 18–24 inches long and weigh 3–4 pounds. They are active feeders, eating most any fish of appropriate size and many invertebrates. Stripers are a popular sport fish.

Sunfish Family (Centrarchidae)

1

a. Body elongated, length 3 times depth

2

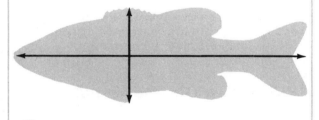

b. Body short and deep, length less than 3 times depth

3

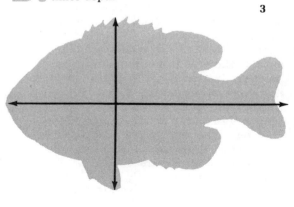

2

a. Upper jaw extends back beyond the eye; spiny section of the dorsal fin is separated from the soft-rayed section by a deep notch extending almost to the base of the fin; body olive on back, fading into green on side to white on belly; dark horizontal band or series of dark blotches extending along side from gill cover to tail

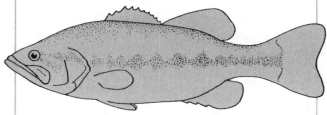

Largemouth Bass *(Micropterus salmoides)*
p. 125

b. Upper jaw does not extend back beyond eye; spiny section of the dorsal fin is not completely separated from soft-rayed section by shallow notch; body greenish brown or bronze; dark vertical markings on sides

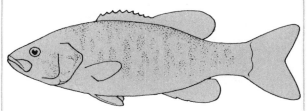

Smallmouth Bass *(Micropterus dolomieui)*
p. 124

3

a. Base of dorsal fin only slightly longer than base of anal fin

4

b. Base of dorsal fin much longer than base of anal fin

5

4

a. Dorsal fin has 7 or 8 spines; distance from eye to front of dorsal fin base about equal to length of dorsal fin base

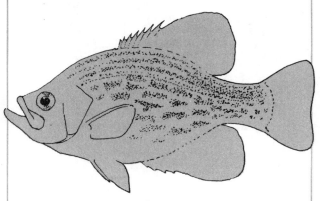

Black Crappie *(Pomoxis nigromaculatus)* p. 126

b. Dorsal fin has 6 spines; distance from eye to front of dorsal fin base greater than length of dorsal fin base

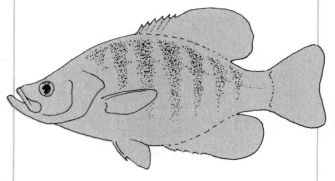

White Crappie *(Pomoxis annularis)* p. 125

5

a. Mouth large, with upper jaw extending back to middle of eye; 6 spines in front portion of anal fin; red eye

Rock Bass *(Ambloplites rupestris)* p. 122

b. Mouth small, with upper jaw not extending back as far as middle of eye; 3 spines in front portion of anal fin; eye not red

6

6

a. Pectoral fin short and rounded

7

b. Pectoral fin long, may be pointed or rounded at tip

8

7

a. Mouth extending back beyond front margin of eye to center of eye; gill flap short and wide; general olive green body color; fins are yellow tipped; body moderately elongated

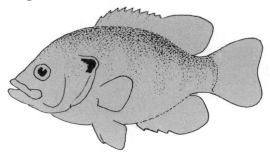

Green Sunfish *(Lepomis cyanellus)* p. 123

b. Mouth extending back only to front margin of eye; gill flap very long; bright flecks of orange or yellow on sides; fins not yellow tipped; body short and deep

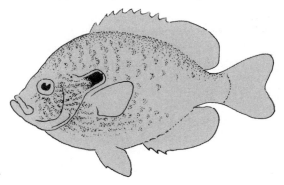

Longear Sunfish *(Lepomis megalotis)* p. 124

8

a. Gill flap with orange, red, or scarlet spot on lower part or tip

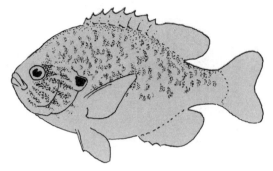

Pumpkinseed Sunfish *(Lepomis gibbosus)* p. 123

b. Gill flap without orange, red, or scarlet spots

9

9

a. Gill flap not as wide as eye, often very long; pectoral fin long, but not pointed; lacks large black spot at rear base of soft-rayed portion of dorsal fin

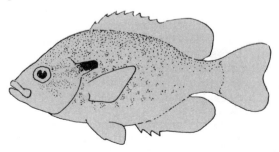

Redbreast Sunfish *(Lepomis auritus)* p. 122

b. Gill flap about as wide as eye, usually not long; pectoral fin long and pointed; has large black spot at rear base of soft-rayed portion of dorsal fin

Bluegill Sunfish *(Lepomis macrochirus)* p. 123

Sunfish Family (Centrarchidae)

The sunfish family includes many of New York's most popular warmwater sport and panfishes. The prized largemouth and smallmouth black basses, the rock bass, and the black crappie and white crappie are all members of this family. Other kinds of sunfish complete the list.

Review of the New York State fishing guide shows that largemouth bass and smallmouth bass are currently managed with specific regulations on size, creel limits, and seasons. These management policies require anglers to identify their catch correctly to apply the proper regulations.

Members of the sunfish family have fins with both soft rays and stiff spines. The dorsal fin, located in the middle of the back, is divided into spiny and soft-rayed sections. The anal fin is located underneath the fish, directly behind the anus. The front section of this fin has three or more spines, and the rear section is soft rayed. The tail is moderately forked. Paired pectoral and pelvic fins are towards the front of the fish. Pelvic fins typically have one spine and are located close together on the underside of the fish, while the pectoral fin on the head is located near the gill cover which protects the fish's gills. New York sunfish have a rearward projection on the gill cover called a gill flap.

Members of the sunfish family can be distinguished readily from salmon and trout because they lack an adipose fin (a small, fatty fin located on the back between the dorsal fin and the tail) characteristic of trout and salmon and because they have fins with stiff spines while trout and salmon have soft-rayed fins only. The difference between members of the sunfish and perch families is not as distinct. However, yellow perch, walleye, and sauger (Percidae) all have the spiny and soft-rayed sections of their dorsal fins separated and have fewer than three anal spines.

All members of the sunfish family but one (Sacramento perch) were naturally distributed east of the Rocky Mountains in the U.S., but stocking programs have increased their distribution to most, if not all, states. Sunfish basically are warmwater inhabitants, preferring, but not being restricted to, fertile lakes with moderate water temperatures and abundant aquatic plants near shore.

Sunfish are spring spawners, with spawning for some species extending into early summer. Males build nests which are saucer-shaped depressions in the lake or stream bottom. Males also guard the eggs and newly hatched young. A few days after they hatch, the young rise out of the nest, at which time the guarding parent leaves them to care for themselves.

All sunfish are carnivorous. Small species and young individuals of larger species eat small invertebrates (such as insects, crustaceans, and mollusks) and small fish. Larger individuals feed heavily on fish and crayfish. The size of fish in this family varies greatly; the longear sunfish seldom reaches 5 inches or weighs more than a few ounces, whereas the largemouth bass may reach 2 feet and exceed 10 pounds.

Rock Bass *(Ambloplites rupestris)*

Rock bass are present in most areas of New York except in the uniformly cold, high-altitude lakes of the Adirondacks. They prefer large lakes with rocky bottoms and streams with sluggish or moderate currents. They often are found in the same habitats as smallmouth bass.

Rock bass are usually 6 to 8 inches in length. They sometimes reach lengths of 10 to 12 inches and weigh 1 pound or more. These fish readily take lures and natural bait; they are scrappy fighters and fine panfish.

Redbreast Sunfish *(Lepomis auritus)*

Redbreast sunfish occur in rivers and lakes of southeastern New York, the Raquette River system, Lake George, and the upper Hudson watershed. It is common in the Chemung, Susquehanna, and Delaware river systems; it is not found on Long Island. These fish do well in rivers where smallmouth bass and rock bass reside. They also inhabit pond and lake environments similar to those preferred by pumpkinseed sunfish, where the two species may be found together. Lengths of 6 to 8 inches are most common for redbreast sunfish, although they may reach lengths of 11 to 12 inches and a weight of about 1 pound. Because they are good fighters for their size, readily take small natural baits and lures, and are good eating, redbreast sunfish are popular panfish in areas where they reach a fair size.

Green Sunfish *(Lepomis cyanellus)*

The green sunfish is found in several areas of New York, excluding the general Adirondack region and Long Island, but is rare. It has been reported from the lower Hudson drainage, Susquehanna River system, and north end of Cayuga Lake. It prefers small, shallow lakes, but is well adapted to all warmwater habitats. This sunfish averages about 6 inches, but may reach a maximum of about 10 inches. Its limited distribution makes it, along with the longear sunfish, less popular as a panfish than other members of the sunfish family in New York.

Pumpkinseed Sunfish *(Lepomis gibbosus)*

The pumpkinseed is the most widely distributed and abundant sunfish in New York, occurring throughout the state including Long Island. They seem to prefer weedy, warmwater lakes and ponds, using weed patches, docks, and logs for cover and usually staying close to shore. They are present in the calm pools of most rivers. The average pumpkinseed is about 5 to 6 inches in length, although some may approach 10 inches.

Pumpkinseeds bite voraciously on nearly any type of natural bait, providing it is small, and on a variety of small artificial lures; flies are especially effective. Their wide distribution, abundance, unhesitating tendency to bite on worms, and close proximity to shore have made them a favorite among youngsters. They make fine eating, but their small size limits their potential as sport fish.

Bluegill Sunfish *(Lepomis macrochirus)*

Bluegills were originally found in western New York and in Lake Champlain, but owing to stocking they are now widely distributed in the state, with the exception of some cold lakes and streams in the Adirondacks. Bluegills frequent calm, weedy waters, with docks, logs, and lily pad beds all providing shelter for these fish. Large bluegills stay in deeper water during the day and move to nearshore areas in morning and evening to feed. They are frequently stocked in farm ponds and other small ponds as forage fish.

Bluegills feed on many forms of natural foods, especially small crustaceans, insects, and plant material. They average 8 inches in length; a few may reach or exceed 10 inches, but these are exceptional. They are spunky, though not spectacular fighters when hooked. Their flesh is delicious, making them one of the most sought-after panfish in New York.

Longear Sunfish *(Lepomis megalotis)*

The longear sunfish is both restricted in its distribution and scarce in New York. It has been reported from the Lake Ontario plain and in tributaries north of Skaneateles and Oneida lakes. This sunfish reaches a maximum length of about 8 inches, 3 to 4 inches being average. It lives in clear, weedy streams, ponds, and bays and is reported to feed principally on aquatic insects. The small-sized longear sunfish is not an important panfish in New York.

Smallmouth Bass *(Micropterus dolomieui)*

Smallmouth bass are not as common as largemouth, but are widely distributed throughout the state, including Long Island. They prefer large, deep lakes or streams with clear water and gravelly or rocky bottoms.

Smallmouth bass are generally smaller than largemouth, but their capacity for resisting capture and their acrobatics when hooked more than make up for any deficiency in size. They rarely exceed 5 pounds in New York, and any fish over 3 pounds is very good. These fish feed on many types of aquatic life and readily take both natural and artificial baits. They are a highly esteemed food and sport fish.

Largemouth Bass *(Micropterus salmoides)*

Largemouth bass are found throughout New York, preferring the shallow, weedy portions of lakes or rivers. They are not as abundant in the Adirondacks as elsewhere; they are common on Long Island. Weedy areas provide both protection and food supplies in the form of forage fish. Water areas of 20 feet or less in depth are optimum.

Largemouth bass in New York only rarely reach a weight of 10 pounds. Usually any fish over 3 pounds is considered a good catch; those over 5 pounds are trophies. Largemouth eat fish, crayfish, frogs, snakes, and some small mammals and young birds if given the opportunity. These fish readily take natural and artificial baits and are good fighters when hooked, making them one of New York's most important sport fish. They are good eating.

White Crappie *(Pomoxis annularis)*

In New York, the white crappie is not nearly as common as the black crappie; it is rare in the Adirondack Mountains and on Long Island. The white crappie is fairly common in the western part of the state including the Allegheny River and Lake Erie drainage systems. It occurs along the Lake Ontario coastal plain west of Rochester. It has been reported in the Mohawk and Hudson River near Albany. It is abundant in a few waters where it occurs, such as the Whitney Point Reservoir. It can live in more turbid water than the black crappie.

These fish are very prolific, and stunted populations often occur. In addition, they are extremely cyclic. Some years they are abundant, but in other years they nearly disappear. This characteristic generally makes the white crappie less important as a sport fish than the black crappie.

Most white crappies are 6 to 12 inches in length and weigh less than 1 pound, although occasionally fish of 2 to 3 pounds are caught. Crappies are schooling fish, active feeders, and can be caught with small artificial or natural baits.

Black Crappie *(Pomoxis nigromaculatus)*

Black crappie populations are found throughout New York, although their distribution is spotty. It is widely distributed in the Allegheny River system, in the tributaries of Lake Erie, along the coastal plain of Lake Ontario, and scattered elsewhere through southern New York including Oneida Lake, the Mohawk River system, the Hudson River, and extreme northeastern New York. It is also in the upper St. Lawrence system and a few localities on Long Island. This fish prefers the quiet waters of lakes, especially those with ample vegetation and clear water.

Black crappie travel in schools, feeding on small fish, aquatic insects, and crustaceans. They may exceed 1 pound in weight and 12 inches in length. More commonly, they average ½ pound and 7 to 10 inches. These little fish are scrappy fighters, but tire quickly. Crappies tend to stay together and several usually can be caught once a school is located. Flies, small poppers, small spinners, and small minnows are good bait.

Perch Family (Percidae)

1

a. Mouth large, upper jaw extending back to middle of eye or beyond; moderate to large fish

2

b. Mouth small, mouth not extending back beyond front margin of eye; small fish never over 6 inches long, usually much smaller

4

2

a. Body olive on back, blending into golden yellow on sides to white on belly, with 6 to 8 distinct, vertical, olive-colored bars extending from the back to below the middle of the sides; lacks oversize fanglike (canine) teeth; pelvic fins close together, with space between them less than width of base of either fin

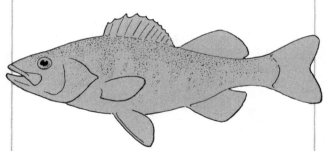

Yellow Perch *(Perca flavescens)* p. 130

b. Body without distinct, vertical, dark bars; elongated, fanglike (canine) teeth present; pelvic fins widely separated by space equal to width of base of either fin

3

3

a. Lower lobe of tail fin with white tip; dark spot at posterior end of spinous dorsal fin; no black spot on base of pectoral fin; greenish or yellowish body color; upper sides and back marked with 6 or more small, dark, saddlelike bands

Walleye *(Stizostedion vitreum)* p. 132

b. Lower lobe of tail fin without white tip, but with dark and white stripes; lacks dark spot at posterior end of spinous dorsal fin, but with small black spots radiating along the spine of the dorsal fin; black spot on base of pectoral fin; general grayish color; sides with 3 or 4 large, dark, saddlelike bands or blotches

Sauger *(Stizostedion canadense)* p. 131

4

a. Anal fin large, equal to or larger than soft dorsal fin; pelvic fins well separated, space between them usually at least ¾ as wide as length of the base of either pelvic fin; tail usually slightly forked; space between bases of pelvic fins and along belly either without scales or with one or more enlarged ctenoid scales; body usually long and shallow

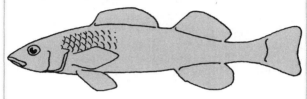

Darters *(Percina* spp.) p. 132

b. Anal fin smaller than soft dorsal fin; distance between pelvic fins usually less than ¾ as wide as length of base of either pelvic fin; tail may be slightly forked, square, or rounded; space between bases of pelvic fins and along belly either with or without scales, but scales never enlarged; body somewhat compressed

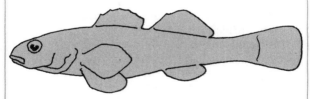

Darters *(Etheostoma* spp.) p. 132

Perch Family (Percidae)

Among New York's popular sport fish are three members of the perch family — yellow perch, walleye, and sauger. The colorful little darters are members of this family, but these small, nongame fish are not often encountered. Walleye are currently managed with specific regulations on size, creel limits, and seasons; in some waters, sauger have a season concurrent with walleye. Because these fish are similar in appearance, anglers must identify their catch correctly to apply the proper regulations and to avoid unintentional violations of fish and wildlife laws.

Members of the perch family have fins with both soft rays and stiff spines. The dorsal fin, located in the middle of the back, is divided into two sections; the front section is spiny and the rear section is soft rayed. The anal fin has two spines in front.

Members of the perch family are readily distinguished from trout and salmon because perch lack an adipose fin, the small fatty fin located on the back of trout and salmon between the dorsal and tail fins. Further, they have a two-part dorsal fin, the first of which is spiny, unlike members of the trout and salmon family or pike family, both of which have single, soft-rayed dorsal fins. Members of the perch family differ from members of the sunfish family on two characters — the two sections of the dorsal fin are distinctly separated, not continuous as in sunfish, and they have two or fewer anal fin spines, not three or more as in sunfish.

Yellow Perch *(Perca flavescens)*

The yellow perch is the most widely distributed member of the perch family and is common throughout New York, including Long Island. Favored habitat of yellow perch is a weedy, warmwater lake. They spawn in the spring when water temperatures are in the 45° to 50°F range. The female swims among sticks and weeds in open, shallow water near shore as she emits a long, gelatinous ribbon of spawn. In this manner, the semibuoyant, adhesive egg mass is woven among the weeds and brush. Males, as many as a dozen, follow the female and fertilize the eggs. Eggs may number from 10,000 to 48,000, depending on the size of the female. No parental care is given to the eggs, which hatch in approximately 3 weeks. Schools of young perch feed on zooplankton. Young perch are slow swimmers, and the schools provide abundant forage for walleye, older yellow perch, and most other predacious fish. Larger yellow perch become important competitors with more highly valued sport fishes in some lakes.

Although the yellow perch is not a fierce fighter when hooked, it is a popular panfish and good eating. Perch seldom reach large sizes, the average being ¼- to ¾-pound fish of 6 to 10 inches. Easily caught on natural bait, flies, and small spinners, they are often the mainstay of ice fishermen using jigs and small minnows. In addition, the yellow perch ranks right along with the various sunfishes as being the impatient young angler's old standby.

Sauger *(Stizostedian canadense)*

Sauger are nearly identical to walleye in most respects. The major difference is that the walleye attains a larger size. Sauger are scarce in New York, occurring primarily in the Great Lakes and Lake Champlain. They have been reported from tributaries of Lake Erie, Cayuga Lake, eastern Lake Ontario, the Mohawk River, and in northeastern New York.

Sauger are slender fish, seldom reaching a length of 18 inches or weight of 3 pounds. Their spawning habits are similar to those of walleye. Their eating habits are also similar. However, aquatic insects are a larger part of the sauger's diet and owing to their smaller size, the sauger consumes smaller fish than the walleye. As a food, they are the equal of walleyes.

Walleye *(Stizostedian vitreum)*

Walleyes are widely distributed in New York State in suitable habitat. They are found in approximately 75 lakes and many large rivers. Walleyes, also called walleyed pike, are the largest members of the perch family, sometimes reaching a length over 2 feet and a weight approaching 20 pounds. Their diet is primarily other fish.

Walleyes prefer large lakes with considerable areas of deep water and large rivers, with cold to moderately warm water temperatures the most favorable. As the surface water approaches 72°F, they slowly retreat to deeper and cooler waters.

Walleyes spawn soon after ice-out when the water temperature is about 45°–50°F. Females move into the spawning area — a stream, shallow area, or shoal — where the males have already congregated. Usually, the spawning area is a location with 1 to 5 feet of clear water in some type of current. The female is attended by several males as they swim over the spawning area, simultaneously emitting eggs and milt as they go. Fertilized eggs fall among the gravel and rocks on the bottom which provide some protection. No parental care is given to either eggs or young.

The walleye is considered by some to be the state's top sport fish, and most agree it is unexcelled as a foodfish.

Darters *Etheostoma* spp. *Percina* spp.)

Probably a dozen or more species of darters are present in New York State. These small fish, 1 to 3 inches in length, are seldom encountered by the average fisherman or naturalist, even though some darters are among the most brightly colored of our freshwater fish. Darters are spring spawners and display a wide variety of spawning behavior. They are probably best known to a few scientists who frequently use these species for behavior studies in the laboratory. Most darters are relatively intolerant of turbid, muddy waters and are very sensitive to chemical pollution and silting.

Drum or Sheepshead Family (Sciaenidae)

Freshwater Drum *(Aplodinotus grunniens)*

The freshwater drum is the only member of the drum family found in fresh water, usually in large rivers and lakes. It typically frequents water 10 to 40 feet deep. Its common name results from its ability to make a drumming, croaking, or rumbling sound from its air bladder and associated muscles.

This fish has a blunt snout and a pronounced humpback appearance. Its long dorsal fin extends from the peak of the hump rearward, nearly reaching the rounded tail. The average size is about 15 inches, although larger specimens of 10 pounds are not rare.

Freshwater drum are found in Lake Erie, along the Lake Ontario plain, in the outlet north of Cayuga Lake, in the tributaries of the St. Lawrence River, and in several locations north of Albany, including Lake George and Lake Champlain.

Spawning occurs in the spring when water temperatures reach 65°–70°F. The eggs are broadcast over shallow gravelly and sandy stretches near shore where they adhere to the bottom. No parental care is given the eggs or young.

Freshwater drum feed heavily on snails, other mollusks, and crayfish. Although the drum can be caught with bait or lures and fights hard, it is not important as a game fish because of its low quality flesh. In most areas it is considered a rough fish, in the same class as carp, with only a minor value in the commercial fishery.

Sculpin Family (Cottidae)

Mottled Sculpin *(Cottus bairdi)*
Slimy Sculpin *(Cottus cognatus)*

Sculpins are small fish, 2 to 3 inches long, having enlarged, flattened heads with eyes placed high on the head and close together. Their pectoral fins are large and they have two dorsal fins. They have no scales on their slippery skin, but a small patch of prickles is present behind the pectoral fin.

There are two sculpins in New York State, the mottled sculpin and the more common slimy sculpin. Mottled sculpin are common from Lake Erie and the Allegheny system in western New York through the Susquehanna River system. Some populations occur in the Genesee River and tributaries of Cayuga Lake. The slimy sculpin prefers cold water and is scattered throughout the state in trout streams. It is especially common in the Catskills and Adirondacks.

These small fish live in cold, clear waters of lakes and streams and are an important part of lake trout and brook trout diets in some waters. Occasionally, they are used as bait. They are omnivores, eating aquatic vegetation and several types of small aquatic animals. Because of their small size and bottom-living habit, they are not well known to most fishermen. Catching a large one (6 inches) on bait is unusual.

References

Brown, C. J. D. 1971. *Fishes of Montana.* Agric. Exp. Sta., Montana State Univ., Bozeman. 207 pp.

Clemens, W. A. and G. V. Wilby. 1949. *Fishes of the Pacific Coast of Canada.* Fish. Res. Board of Canada, Ottawa. 368 pp.

Decker, D. J., R. A. Howard, Jr., and J. W. Kelley. 1978. *Let's go fishing.* 4-H Leaders' Guide, L-5-6. N.Y.S. Coll. of Agric. and Life Sci., Cornell Univ., Ithaca. 33 pp.

Eddy, S. 1957. *How to know the freshwater fishes.* Wm. C. Brown, Co., Dubuque, Iowa. 253 pp.

Eddy, S. and T. Surber. 1960. *Northern fishes.* Revised edition. Charles T. Branford Co., Newton Centre 50, Mass. 276 pp.

Everhart, W. H. 1966. *Fishes of Maine.* 3rd edition. Maine Dept. of Inland Fisheries and Game. 96 pp.

Everhart, W. H. and W. R. Seaman. 1971. *Fishes of Colorado.* Colorado Game, Fish and Parks Div., Denver. 75 pp.

Greeley, J. R. 1955. *Our black basses.* N.Y. Conservationist. June –July 1955 (reprint). 2 pp.

Hubbs, C. L. and K. F. Lagler. 1947. *Fishes of the Great Lakes region.* Cranbrook Inst. of Sci. Bull. 26. 186 pp.

McClane, A. J. 1965. *McClane's standard fishing encyclopedia.* Holt, Rinehart and Winston, Inc., New York. 1057 pp.

N.Y.S. Sea Grant Extension. 1977. *What's it?: a guide for identification of Great Lakes salmon and trout in New York.* Leaflet.

Raney, E. C. Articles from the N.Y. Conservationist:
1949. *Perch.* 3(6):15.
1954. *The striped bass in New York waters.* 8(4):14 –16.
1959. *Some young freshwater fishes of New York.* 14(1):22 –28.
1965. *Some pan fishes of New York —yellow perch, white perch, white bass, and freshwater drum.* 19(5):22 –28.
1965. *Some pan fishes of New York — rock bass, crappies, and other sunfishes.* 19(6):21 –29.
1967. *Some catfishes of New York.* June –July (reprint). 7pp.
1969. *Minnows of New York. Part 1: Facts about some of our chubs and dace.* 23(5):22 –29.
1969. *Minnows of New York. Part 2: The shiners.* 23(6):21 –29.

Scott, W. B. 1967. *Freshwater fishes of eastern Canada.* Univ. of Toronto Press. 137 pp.

Scott, W. B. and E. J. Crossman. 1973. *Freshwater fishes of Canada.* Bulletin 184, Fisheries Research Board of Canada, Ottawa. 966 pp.

Index to Scientific Names

136

Index to Common Names

138

Metric Conversion Charts for Length, Weight and Temperature

When you know	Multiply by	To find
inches	2.5	centimeters
ounces	28	grams
pounds	0.45	kilograms
Fahrenheit temperature	5/9 (after subtracting 32)	Celsius (°C) temperature

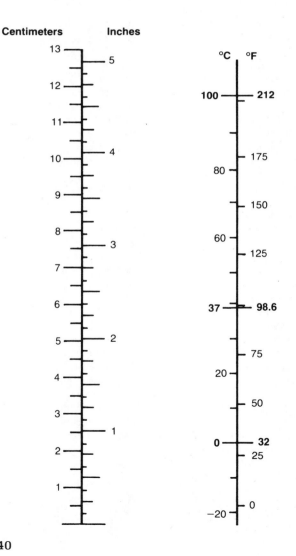